# NIGHTMARE IN DUBLIN

# NIGHTMARE
## *in*
# DUBLIN

### *By Philip Loraine*

he M. S. Mill Company and William Morrow & Company
New York

# CONTENTS

———————————— "*John Kevin's Dublin*," wrote one of the critics, "is without doubt the least successful and the least popular of his remarkable series. Many of his admirers were dumbfounded to discover that for this artist in photography the 'fair city' of the ballad was a haunted place of strange shadows and grotesque images. Bizarre. Often downright sinister. Exactly why it appeared to him in this light must remain a mystery, since he refuses to explain himself. . . ."

*part one:* **THE DREAM OF DEATH**

———————— I

THE PAGE BOY'S VOICE—a banshee wailing
in some mist-haunted bog—rose above the polite chatter of
the bar and hung there unhappily. The boy himself was
still some distance away; if anybody in the room had understood the wording of the wail, and this was doubtful,
he paid no attention. The chatter rose up like a wave, was
gathered into a glittering crest of laughter, and broke over
John Kevin's head, which was supported in his two hands.
His elbows rested on the counter, and his expression was
one of resignation; he was resigned because he realized that
he had taken several dry Martinis too many, and that all
desire to eat had now forsaken him. Since it was now past
ten o'clock he would probably continue to drink dry
Martinis.

He looked at himself in the mirror behind the bar and
was relieved to see that he looked perfectly healthy and
perfectly sober. He was brown from the French sun, and his
eyebrows and hair were slightly bleached—slightly too
fair, he thought privately; the eyebrows were merely absurd, but the hair (he thought privately) gave him the look

of a retired chorus boy who had put on weight. He had therefore had most of it cut off. The result was vaguely reminiscent of a Black Forest holiday-maker, which was only slightly preferable to the previous state. With his height and his very fair curly hair, people stared at him—particularly, he noticed, dark, small women.

Again the page boy's voice was raised, this time much nearer, and, as if the banshee were indeed calling them, a small cold silence fled through the drinkers, and was chased away by another burst of laughter.

John Kevin closed his eyes. At once he was in the plane again, bumping most uncomfortably over an iron-grey sea. It had been a bad flight; the bumps had persisted all the way from Paris to Dublin, seeming that they would presently wrench the wings off the airliner.

The page boy appeared in the doorway. He surveyed the assembled drinkers with bright, black, appraising eyes; the expression on his face indicated that he didn't think much of what he saw. Again he wailed; he wailed twice—and once more.

At the third performance it occurred to John Kevin that this "Misser Cur-ur-ur-vin" was no other than himself. He opened his eyes and returned from the bouncing plane to the elegant Georgian cocktail bar of the Melbourne Hotel, Dublin, Eire. He beckoned to the boy.

"Did you say Kevin?"

"I did, sor." The tone implied more.

"What is it?"

"A—gentleman to see you, sor."

"What's his name?" he asked automatically, but he knew

4

that only one man in Ireland would be asking for him. Stephen Lawlor.

The page boy's eyes brightened suddenly, and he replied, "It's the guard, sor."

"The—"

"The police, sor."

John Kevin nodded. He had been in Dublin exactly two and a half hours in the whole of his life, and the police were asking for him! It was not, in the rough-and-tumble life he led, an unusual occurrence, but it generally took a week at the least to come about. He rose wearily from his stool and followed the boy out of the room. The floor of the passage, like the floor of the plane, bucked under his feet. He had never been good at air travel, and then of course five Martinis on an empty stomach . . .

The page led him to a door marked *Private* and admitted him to a small office, wailing as he did so, "Misser Kevin, sor."

John Kevin looked at the guard—represented in this instance by a short, grizzle-haired man in a tweed suit and mackintosh, and a tall young sergeant in uniform—and the guard looked at John Kevin. An assistant manager, subdued in black, glanced from one to the other apprehensively.

When the guard smiled John Kevin smiled also; the assistant manager was relieved, and smiled as well.

"Is it my cameras?" said Kevin. "It quite often is."

The grey-haired man shook his head.

"No, sir. That'd be a Customs matter." He came forward. "My name's O'Connor. Chief Inspector. I'm sorry to trouble you so soon after your arrival."

5

"No trouble," replied Kevin, trying not to sway.

"You know a Mr. Lawlor, sir—a Mr. Stephen Lawlor."

"Yes, I do. What's he been up to?"

"Is he a close friend?"

"Hardly. Used to be once. I met him in Paris a couple of weeks ago. Otherwise we hadn't seen each other for five years."

O'Connor nodded.

"Why?" said Kevin.

The two policemen glanced away suddenly as if controlled by the same nervous system.

"Mr. Lawlor's dead, sir."

There was a close silence in the small room. Finally Kevin said, "I see." He was surprised, shocked in fact, to find that Steve Lawlor, dead, was in some way not a surprising thing. He would have to think about that later; it doubtless had something to do with the mixture of braggadocio, moody silence, foolhardiness and sentimentality which had gone to make up the man's character.

Kevin said, "How?"

"An accident, sir."

Kevin glanced up sharply and met the Inspector's grey, straight eyes; they did not waver, and yet there had been in his forming of the word "accident" something a fraction out of true—a rising inflection, perhaps, which posed the merest breath of question.

"A car accident?"

O'Connor nodded. "'You would expect that?"

"Oh, yes. He always liked speed. Danger."

Again there was silence.

6

Was it, Kevin wondered, the Martinis, or was there in this airless room a faint overtone of menace?

Perhaps his expression revealed something of doubt, for Inspector O'Connor began to talk suddenly, as if, menace or no, he wished to keep things normal.

"I understand that Mr. Lawlor was over here to see his aunt, Miss Bella Lawlor of Drumnagh."

"He did say something about her in Paris."

"Yes." O'Connor looked interested. "You see, our trouble is identification. Although he arrived over a week ago, Miss Lawlor has seen nothing of him." The Inspector clearly thought this odd. Kevin, remembering that Steve Lawlor expected to be left Aunt Bella's Georgian mansion and her money, thought it odd also. "There's no doubt," the Inspector added, "that he was on his way to Drumnagh —that's the aunt's house—when the accident occurred. He never got there. It's fifteen years since she last saw him— he'd have been little more than a boy—and it seems hardly sensible to ask her to identify the body. Particularly—" He looked pained suddenly. "Particularly as it's rather a mess."

Kevin gulped.

"There was a letter from you in Mr. Lawlor's pocket, saying that you'd be staying at this hotel from the tenth, so we thought . . ."

"I see," said Kevin.

"The aunt," pursued O'Connor, "is getting on in years, and naturally I would prefer not to trouble her, particularly in this case because, as I said, it's not the most pleasant identi- fication I've come across. Mind you, for a man it's easier. I daresay this isn't the first time you've . . ."

7

Was it, Kevin wondered, merely a national characteristic to make all this talk over the mere formality of identification? Or was it merely national kindliness tiding over an ugly situation? Or was it more? Did something lie behind the talk? Something menacing?

". . . and so it's really a bit of luck for us that you should be here at the moment. Of course, identification's only a formality, but then so is the rest of our job for the most part."

Kevin, suddenly impatient, said, "I'll identify him. Where is he?"

The police car lurched and bucked through thick, driving rain. The Wicklow Mountains were nothing but black, shapeless monsters crouched in the night.

"A pity," said O'Connor brightly, "for this is a peach of a drive on a fine day, and the visitors flock here in thousands."

Kevin grunted.

"You said," the policeman went on, "that you knew Stephen Lawlor well."

"Five years ago, yes."

"And you met again in Paris?"

"Yes."

"You saw something of him there."

"Enough," said Kevin, "to recognize him now—if that's what you mean."

The car lurched.

"Damn," said Kevin out loud. First of all the bucking plane, and now this; it was too much.

"Would you care," O'Connor pursued, "to tell me something about the man?"

"Why?" Lack of food, the five Martinis and continuing physical discomfort were scraping a raw edge to his temper. The police of several countries could have told O'Connor about the John Kevin temper.

"Why?" echoed the Inspector. "Well, when a man dies suddenly various questions naturally present themselves. There is always the chance of suicide, for instance."

"In a car?"

"He drove it," added O'Connor dryly, "over a two-hundred-foot cliff—through a stone wall, too."

"Drunk probably."

"I think not."

Kevin turned and stared at the man. With his grizzled head and lean features he looked more like a country farmer than a policeman. His tweed suit gave off a pleasant country smell; his eyes were as hard as two granite pebbles, washed and washed and washed in a thundering ocean of mistrust.

"It strikes me," said Kevin finally, "that you think Steve Lawlor was up to something. As soon as I came into that office at the hotel I got a—a feeling."

O'Connor said nothing for some time. The car continued its prancing journey. Then: "Mr. Kevin, would you care to tell me why you're here in Ireland?"

"Guess," replied Kevin savagely. "These *bloody* roads!"

"Did you, for instance, have an appointment with Mr. Lawlor?"

"You've got the letter I wrote to him, haven't you?"

9

"It merely says that you would be staying at the Melbourne."

"Exactly."

"Mr. Lawlor asked you to visit him?"

"Damnation!" snapped Kevin. "What minds you policemen have. What a lot of extra work you give yourselves through disbelieving *everything*. I met Steve Lawlor in Paris; I said I was going to Dublin; he said so was he, because his aunt had expressed a desire to see him; I said we must meet there; he said yes we must. Isn't that the most suspicious thing you ever heard?"

"Your temper," said O'Connor mildly, "must've got you in plenty of trouble."

"It has."

"And why *are* you in Dublin, sir?"

"Ah." Kevin beat a fist on his knee. "You're never going to believe this—I'm here to take photographs."

"So I thought. There was a paragraph about you in the *Herald*. I'm told your work is well-known all over the world."

"We've got a nice racket," admitted the young man, still savage. "*John Kevin's Rome. John Kevin's Tyrol.* John Kevin's This and bloody That. I've *done* Paris, and now I'm doing Dublin—if the rain stops."

"We've some lovely buildings. You've seen the Bank, no doubt."

"Buildings and faces," said John Kevin bitterly. "It's so damn easy it gives me the pip. People think it's clever. You take an old woman who's lived on gin for thirty years and put her in front of an elegant baroque façade. Or a fashion model sitting on the steps of a slum. It's all a

10

bloody sham. Any nitwit can take a good photograph, anyway."

The car skidded into a rut, leapt and shuddered.

"Hell," said Kevin. "Aren't we nearly there?"

"Yes, we are. Would you like a drop of whisky? I've a flask here."

Kevin glanced at him. "D'you think I need it?"

O'Connor nodded. "You may. I should warn you that Mr. Lawlor— Well, he fell two hundred feet—and the car caught fire."

After a moment the young man said, "Hell, I wish I'd had some dinner."

The little police station at Rathlaw was a gloomy box of grey stone. There was a distinct doing-up of buttons and straightening of caps attendant upon Inspector O'Connor's arrival. He stood in the centre of the bare room and glared round uncomfortably. He looked, Kevin thought, more than ever like a small, angry farmer; but there was a power and a kind of ferocious orderliness about him which made his taller subordinates appear rough and shambling.

"Now, Mr. Kevin," he said. "Before we look at the body, you'll tell me perhaps how you'd identify Mr. Stephen Lawlor." He held up a hand to stop the young man from speaking. "I'd better warn you straight away that the head and shoulders are badly burned."

Kevin nodded, but his mouth had gone dry suddenly. "There was a birthmark," he said. "In the small of his back —well, higher up, really—just above the waist. L-shaped."

O'Connor nodded.

"He always used that as his official distinguishing mark —for his wartime identity papers and so on."

11

"Anything else?"

"Not that I know of. Signet ring, of course. A swan sitting on one of those sticks of barley sugar."

"Dental work?"

"Really, I've no idea."

"Clothes?"

"Sometimes he looked scruffy, sometimes he looked smart. I couldn't say."

"Anything that you know he happened to buy in Paris? Wearing apparel, I mean?"

"Only ties—that I know of. I was with him when he got them."

"Describe them if you can."

Kevin felt trapped, yet there could be no trap. He moistened his lips. "One was blue, in silk, with sort of formalized sea gulls on it in white. Another had an interlinking chain pattern, black and grey on white. Ghastly."

"Did he wear a watch?"

"Heavens, yes. Never stopped telling everyone that he'd had it for fifteen years or something. A Rolex."

O'Connor nodded again, and turned towards a door in the corner. One of the guard opened it, and John Kevin, bracing himself, followed the trim figure into an even greyer, barer room.

The body—unpleasantly shapeless under a sheet—lay on a table. O'Connor lifted the sheet from the lower end. The shoes, socks, suit were at once familiar to Kevin. "Yes," he said. The sheet rose higher, revealing the scorched tip of a silk tie—white gulls on a blue background; a wrist, nastily burned, with a Rolex watch strapped round it. On the

12

blackened little finger, gold glinted. There was a stench of petrol and fire.

O'Connor dropped the sheet and said to the guard, "Turn him over. Sorry. We must."

Kevin looked away. He felt extremely sober now—and sick.

"Lift up the clothes," said O'Connor. "Gently. . . . Ah. . . ." After a pause he added, "Once more, Mr. Kevin, please. The birthmark."

The young man looked, nodded. "Yes, that's him, all right." Then he turned and walked out of the cell back to the larger room. He sat down abruptly on a bench and leaned against the wall, eyes closed. The world around him heaved and dipped as it had done on the plane, and, apparently, ever since.

"I'm sorry," said O'Connor's voice. "Very nasty, I agree. Formality, you understand." He sounded most unwell himself. To someone else he said, "Ryan, I don't want that car touched until I've seen it in the morning; keep a guard on it all night."

Kevin opened his eyes and stared. O'Connor returned the stare unwinkingly. "Now," he said, "if you're ready, Mr. Kevin, sir, we'll be getting back to Dublin."

In the car Kevin said, "You don't think it was an accident, do you?"

O'Connor sighed. "Mr. Lawlor liked driving, you say; he liked speed. That kind of man doesn't run himself over a cliff in a nice new car, cold stone sober. He doesn't, Mr. Kevin, really he doesn't."

"But Steve Lawlor wouldn't commit *suicide*. It's— It's nonsensical."

13

O'Connor nodded. "Ah, I'm inclined to agree with you," he said, almost primly.

"Then—"

O'Connor did not reply. He pointed vaguely through the streaming darkness. "On a fine day," he said, "you get a wonderful view from here. Glenmalure, you know—and Lugnaquilla beyond. That's one of our highest—over three thousand feet. What a pity you can't see it, for it's a lovely sight."

"You mean," said Kevin, "that you think somebody killed him."

O'Connor stared out of the window in the rough direction of his "wonderful view." He did not reply.

## II

Kevin opened his eyes and shut them again quickly. A long blunt needle threaded itself through his head. He groaned. The taste of whisky was still in his mouth.

The telephone shrilled again hysterically. He stretched out a hand and felt for it, then laid the receiver near his ear and croaked, "Hullo."

"Mr. Kevin?"

"Yes."

"A lady to see you, sir."

"I don't know any ladies in Dublin."

"A Miss Celia Dillon, sir."

Kevin groaned again. "No, no. You've got the wrong Kevin. Not me. Give me Room Service."

"Very good, sir."

As soon as he had ordered black coffee from Room Service and Alka-Seltzer from the porter, the telephone went off into hysterics again.

"Hullo. Kevin here."

15

"Mr. Kevin, Miss Dillon insists that it is you she wishes to see. Will you speak to her?"

"I will not. I'm ill. Tell her I'm ill."

He lay back and closed his eyes. Everything was wrong; everything had gone wrong from the moment he had set foot in the plane. Dublin had a jinx on it; presently he would get up and find, doubtless, that his camera was broken. Miss Celia Dillon indeed!

It had been weakness, of course, to start drinking whisky after his return from Rathlaw and the unpleasant business of Steve Lawlor's body. But the unpleasantness pursued him; that, and the bumping plane, and no dinner, and five Martinis and then the ride in that lurching police car. And so—whisky.

The coffee arrived, silently and with discretion. An inch of curtain was drawn back, no more. Dublin was evidently not unused to the effects of alcohol upon visitors.

Querulously Kevin said, "I want my Alka-Seltzer."

"The page is bringing it, sir."

"Thank heaven."

But no sooner had the door closed upon the chamber-maid than voices were raised outside it—a genteel gaggle of voices culminating in one clear statement delivered in the crystal tones of confident young girlhood: "Now, my good souls," it said, "let me in, for I'm his sister and he needs me."

With which astonishing assertion the door flew open and Miss Celia Dillon—Alka-Seltzer in one hand, fending off the page boy with the other—arrived. She shut the door firmly behind her and bolted it.

16

Kevin regarded her in silence—what he could see of her.

"Miss Dillon," he said.

"Yes. I—" Her composure seemed to have deserted her. She held out the Alka-Seltzer.

Kevin said, "Water. Three tablets. They dissolve quicker if it's warm."

Miss Dillon obeyed.

"Then," said Kevin distantly, "ring the bell for the manager and have yourself thrown out."

The girl came back from the washbasin and put the fizzing glassful on the bedside table. "I've got to talk to you," she said. "I can wait. I know you must feel awful, but I've got to talk to you."

In the curtained room, she was indistinct. Only the voice was clear, and it was touching also; it had the freshness of extreme youth. It was, Kevin thought, irritatingly ladylike, yet there was to it a touch of brogue wholly delightful. His head was splitting.

"Tell me," he croaked, "are you pretty? You sound it."

"I am—in a way," replied the light, young voice.

"Then draw the curtain back a bit more. I'll look at you."

She did so. He saw a bell of pale-gold hair framing a pale-gold face—gold from sunshine—a child's face. The eyes, however, were not blue, but a deep dark brown, and thus surprising. She wore a grey coat and skirt and a white jumper. She looked about eighteen, and well-behaved.

All this he noted in a flash, with the eye of an artist, for, in his own way, he *was* an artist.

"Not pretty at all," he said, turning away from the

17

light. "Arresting. Different. Probably attractive. Much better than being pretty."

"I must talk to you," she said—and suddenly there was anguish in the clear voice. Or perhaps it had been there all along, only now he recognized it for the first time.

"Wait. Wait two minutes." He drank the Alka-Seltzer and poured out a cup of coffee—black and aromatic, healing by the very smell of it.

After a few sips, he said, "Well?"

But there was no answer. He turned, surprised, and found that she had a handkerchief pressed to her face. She was crying.

"Hell!" said Kevin. "Don't do that. I'm sorry if I've been rude."

She shook her head, the pale hair swinging furiously. Then she blew her nose manfully—on, he noticed, a man-size handkerchief.

"It's about Steve," she said. "There— There's no one else I could go to."

Kevin sat up. "I'm an idiot. You knew Steve Lawlor?"

"I— I loved him."

"You did?" The picture was not somehow credible. Nothing about the death of Stephen Lawler was wholly credible, for that matter. Nothing about Dublin either. It all had the ghastly, sane madness of dream.

Then, still snuffling, she said, "There was a bit about you—about you identifying him—in the paper."

"Oh, there was."

She nodded. And suddenly she looked up, brown eyes wildly intense in her child's face. "Someone killed him; that's what happened. I know. I know for certain."

18

"I see."

"Steve was a wonderful driver, and that corner's not even a difficult one."

"He might have been drunk."

She shook her head. "He wasn't. And he wasn't unhappy, either. Anyway, Steve would *never* commit suicide. It's a ridiculous idea."

"I agree."

"You do?" She stood up abruptly and moved towards him. Then stopped. "You— You were Steve's friend; he spoke to me about you."

"So you think he was murdered?"

She shuddered. "Yes, I do."

"Any idea why?"

"No. Except that—"

He watched her now, carefully. The pain in his head had diminished a little; he was interested. "Except that what?"

"He was *doing* something—here in Dublin, I mean. Something—secret," she ended lamely.

"He always was. He loved secrets, dramas, heroics." His interest waned suddenly, at the memory of Stephen Lawlor's histrionic genius.

She glared at him. "Steve was a fine man."

"In some ways, yes." Because she still glared he said, "How long had you known him?"

At this she glanced away. "We— We met in London in the spring. He's only been over here a fortnight. I mean—"

Kevin was pleased about this; she had obviously been under the irresistible Lawlor spell for a very short time—

say, two weeks in London and two weeks in Dublin—and the hurt of his death would not therefore go very deep. Yet she *was* hurt; that was clear in all she said and did. He must pull himself together and handle her carefully—get rid of her gently, for, really, he had no time for her or her grief. He was here on a job—*John Kevin's Dublin* should prove simple. Already he had caught quick, dramatic impressions of the city's blend of squalor and richness, simplicity and sophistication; the graceful Georgian face of it delighted him. Of course he was sorry about Stephen Lawlor's death; it was sad to know that all that gaiety, zest and charm were stilled forever. But Kevin had fought in a war; better men than Lawlor had died before his very eyes. Since then, his sense of values had remained different— distorted possibly, but irretrievably different.

"You should go to the guard," he said. "I'm no use to you." He steeled himself against her very evident disappointment. "And I'll tell you something. They've got roughly the same idea that you have. Ask to see a fellow called O'Connor. Inspector O'Connor. *He* doesn't think it was an accident, either."

The girl turned away and looked out of the window. And suddenly, very much in spite of himself, an overwhelming flood of pity surged up out of the bedroom floor and engulfed John Kevin. And this was all because of her shoulders, which were thin and somehow bowed, and childlike. Gazing out of the window, she squared them—a small movement of courage and defiance, and that also was infinitely moving. He would not look at her, but was aware of the fact that she had turned to face him again.

20

"All right," she said. "I'll go to the guard then. I only thought—" Her eyes were rather fierce now. "I thought that perhaps you'd loved Steve a bit, in your own sort of way, I mean. I thought—"

She walked across to the door and unbolted it.

"Of course," she said, "you're here on business, aren't you? Steve gave me two of your books. They really are beautiful."

This, as it were, *social* courage, added to the rest, was nearly the last straw for John Kevin, weakened as he was by the Demon's hangover and pity.

"I . . ." he began.

"Of course," she said, "I can see that your photographs must be very precious to you." She implied to a nicety that any deeper, more human partiality was obviously outside his ken.

Oddly enough this angered him. Suddenly acid, he said, "And which two books of mine did Stephen Lawlor give you? It wouldn't have been *Rome* and *Edinburgh*, would it?"

"Yes. Yes, it was." She stared. "How did you know?"

"Because," said Kevin, still smarting from her attack, "those were the two I gave him in Paris."

After a small, cold silence, she said, "What a contemptible thing to say. I suppose it's possible to *buy* copies of your masterpieces?"

"Yes, indeed." (So, he was thinking, she hasn't really any idea of the sort of man Stephen Lawlor was.) "Yes, indeed. Fifteen shillings at all the best bookstores."

"Well, then . . ."

21

"But," he said. "Not *Edinburgh*, you see. It isn't being published until next month."

He was ashamed of himself for this, noticing how her face became rigid, but on the other hand he had seen too many women drowned in the Lawlor charm. It bored him.

Miss Celia Dillon, after another pause, said, "Steve may or may not have been all I thought him; I don't care much. But he certainly had some odd friends."

And she slammed the door behind her.

He liked Dublin. Now that the headache had left him he merely felt dreamy, unreal, as if his head were full of cotton wool. Impressions were in some way blunted, and yet paradoxically more intense—as in a dream. He had noticed this before: the aftereffects of alcohol made him impersonal, so that he saw people and buildings with the eye of total strangeness. He therefore took several masterly photographs, including one, in Pearse Street outside the railway station, of a row of hansom cabs with street loungers in the foreground grouped about a lamppost. The angle was low; the ancient cabs receded in violent perspective; the loungers towered, their surprised, sharp, dishonest faces turned anxiously towards him as he knelt with his camera.

It struck him suddenly that if he were to keep this angle on the city—to heighten the drama of it by using odd perspectives, unlikely viewpoints—he might vary the formula: *A Dream of Dublin*. He liked the idea; it suited his mood; it suited, he was inclined to think, the city itself.

He found the buildings unusually positive—even for the

22

eighteenth century—and the people strangely elusive, like the vast sky above them: a cloudy sky of incredible grandeur. Ireland made him more aware of the sky than even Holland, where it was everything.

The little man materialized improbably at his elbow on the northwest corner of Merrion Square.

He said, "Excuse me, sir, but would you not be Mr. Kevin? Mr. John Kevin, and a friend of Stephen Lawlor, God rest his soul?"

The dream, clearly, persisted.

"I am."

The little man nodded. He was stringy, sandy, indeterminate. His clothes hung on him limply, and his thin neck emerged from a too-large collar like the neck of a scrawny chicken. The head was birdlike also, angular and sharp like an ancient vulture's. And the eyes were black and bright and, Kevin thought, not entirely sane.

"A great loss," said this person. "Not often is a man gifted with such fire and unselfishness."

Kevin stared. This was not his idea of Stephen Lawlor at all.

"A great and terrible loss." The eyes grew brighter, as if presently they would catch fire. "A loss to the world, Mr. Kevin. Mark me, a loss to the world. May the blessed Saints watch over him in his torment."

Kevin said, "A most interesting view. You knew him well, no doubt."

"I knew him," said the old vulture, "as I know myself—imperfectly, you understand, but with a deep, deep knowledge." He paused, mouth slightly open.

Can I, Kevin was thinking, oh, can I take a quick one

23

of him as he is now, against the magnificent, imperturbable façade of Merrion Square? On the whole he thought this was not possible.

"A great and terrible man," said the other, flapping his arms against his sides. "A fighter, Mr. Kevin. A seeker after Truth. A crusader for Freedom, sir, with a flaming sword of Truth in his hand. And—" the voice rose, trembling— "and not afraid to *strike*."

He stared curiously into the young man's astonished face for what seemed a long while. Then his gaze shifted, finding something over Kevin's shoulder. The fire died in his brilliant eyes. He wheeled abruptly and walked away with surprising speed, his roomy clothes flapping about his bones.

Kevin, turning with interest to discover what had caused the metamorphosis, saw on the opposite corner, with his back turned, a policeman.

Even this odd encounter might not have disturbed John Kevin, in his mood of photographic creation. He was caught up in his dream of Dublin; on every side the compositions flung themselves at his astounded eyes: the buildings, so evocative of Georgian certainty that man was supreme in all he did; the people, seeming to float impermanently through such grandeur; the tumultuous sky, now clear, now piling up into vast monoliths of Atlantic cloud. No. Even the meeting with an old, mad vulture in Merrion Square might not have disturbed the mood. He turned dreamily, dazzled by those great houses, into Lower Fitzwilliam Street, into Erne Street. And there, by the railway bridge, somebody tried to kill him.

At one moment he was standing on the pavement, sight-

24

ing his camera through the deep shadow of the bridge, down the long vista of sad houses to the River Liffey. He was waiting for a mountainous cloud formation to place itself to his liking, and this necessitated a constant peeping through the view finder. At one moment he was thus engaged, intent, concentrated. At the next he was flying towards the centre of the road, and the entire world had narrowed down to one agonized close-up of a large lorry, head on. A terrible screaming of brakes. The driver's frightened face. Cobblestones spinning. A grab at his precious camera. An excruciating pain. Nothing.

## III

HE WAS ANGRY, and he was determined. What had once been the dull headache of hangover was now the blind, bludgeoning pain of contact with cobblestones. He realized, of course, that he was lucky to be alive at all; but that—like thinking about other people's grief to assuage one's own—was meagre compensation.

The camera, true enough, was in one piece, but his new and expensive exposure metre tinkled merrily when he shook it. He was in a mad rage.

The lorry driver, a nice youth from Cork, barely understandable, had been upset but disinclined to believe that the man he had so nearly killed had been deliberately pushed under his wheels. He took the attitude that such a blow on the head, coupled with shock, might induce the victim to think wild thoughts. And certainly, under the deep shadow of the bridge, he had seen no lurking assassin. For that matter he had not seen Kevin himself until the last moment, and then only because he appeared reeling in silhouette against the bright road beyond.

Now, fuming, Kevin was on his way to see Inspector

O'Connor of the Civic Guard. He had no very clear idea of what he intended to say, but words seethed inside him.

It was as he turned onto the quay and met the raw stink of the Liffey at low water that the fourth strange thing of the morning happened to him—stranger than the advent of Miss Celia Dillon, stranger than the encounter with the old vulture in Merrion Square, stranger even than that vicious blow between the shoulder blades which had all but ended his life. Stranger, because less explicable. In point of fact it was not explicable at all.

He saw a small tavern, wedged between two larger houses—offices by the look of them. The name *Tara Lounge* was written in black on an orange board over the door. It was identical to a hundred other Dublin "lounges"; it was in no way remarkable. And yet a brilliant spark of knowledge flashed in his brain, blinding him, causing him to stop dead and to stare open-mouthed.

He could not for the life of him find any ghost of a reason, any flicker of intelligence, as to why the Tara Lounge should move him thus. And yet, beyond any shadow of doubt, there had been that sudden flash of recognition—and of something deeper than recognition. He had no doubt at all that in the Dublin nightmare, which had started with (which was directly attributable to) that bumping airliner from Paris, the Tara Lounge stood for something vital and incredible.

So strong was this conviction, so maddening the blankness which followed it, that all anger left him completely; he was no longer the least interested in seeing Inspector O'Connor. This public house, though meaningless to him, had suddenly drawn the last eighteen hours into a tight

27

knot. His arrival in Dublin, Stephen Lawlor's death, Celia Dillon, the old vulture, attempted murder under the railway bridge—all were made sensible by the Tara Lounge. No, not sensible; far from sensible; there was no atom of sense in them. Yet, in this strange way, he *felt* them as one homogeneous whole because of the Tara Lounge.

Almost automatically, walking in his dream, he crossed the quay and went into the bar.

"For the love of God," said the barman, "and you still on your two feet, it's a miracle."

John Kevin stared.

"And, sure, you look rough, sor. You'll not mind me saying it."

Kevin examined himself in a fly-blown mirror upon which were engraved two whisky bottles, and for the first time that morning he was aware of himself. He looked, he thought, outlandish. People in Dublin dressed soberly; he, in the jeans and American Navy peajacket which were his working dress, looked positively mythical. Very brown, very tall, very fair, with white eyebrows. He was shocked.

"Will it be whisky, sor?"

"It will not."

"Sure, you had a load on you last night, me boy. If it hadn't been for Shaun O'Farrell I doubt if you'd have found your hotel at all."

"Shaun O'Farrell, eh?"

"Sure, it was him took you there. And you swearing and blinding and reciting whole pages of Shakespeare as though you were the reincarnation of the poet himself."

"Indeed."

The barman chuckled. "Ah, it was a rare show."

28

Kevin, who did not drink often, and very seldom in excess, was ashamed. Ashamed, but at the same time interested. The Tara Lounge meant something to him; he was sure of that now. Somewhere here was a cause, or an effect, of Stephen Lawlor's death. Things were stirring uneasily in the brain behind his consciousness, and he was suddenly excited for no reason he could quite diagnose. O'Connor and the child Celia Dillon thought that Lawlor had been murdered. He, Kevin, *knew* that someone had tried to push him under a lorry. And the answer was here, *here*. He stared, rather wildly, round the shabby bar as if daring it to produce evidence. An old man in the corner—part of last night's audience, no doubt—smiled and winked cordially. The bar remained impassive; it was keeping its secrets to itself.

"Sitting out there, you were," said the barman, still chuckling. "Oh, long after we'd shut. Sitting on the wall there crying out about Birnam Wood, with Shaun O'Farrell hanging onto your legs lest you toppled over backwards into the water."

"This O'Farrell," said Kevin. "Will he be in the bar this morning?"

"No, he will not. For he works out at Clontarf. But this evening he'll be in, I've no doubt."

"About what time?"

"Generally about eight or a little after."

"I'll be here."

He was wildly excited now, though still for no reason he could fathom. Moreover he knew just where he was going, even if (here again) the *reason* was obscure.

He was going to the Wicklow Mountains, to a bend in

29

the road that led to Drumnagh, just above the little town of Rathlaw. He was going to see just where Stephen Lawlor had driven himself through a stone wall and over a two-hundred-foot cliff to his death.

The taxi was ramshackle; he had chosen it because the driver was young, with a wild light in his eye. Now, racketing once more over the road to Rathlaw, he wondered whether he would not have done better to take more note of the vehicle and less of the driver.

However, his mind was full of problems, and presently he became oblivious of all but the most spectacular jolts. He was trying to recall what he knew of Stephen Lawlor, for surely the explanation must lie somewhere in that odd, exasperating, lovable personality.

Stephen Cormac McFadden Lawlor, he thought. Age: something between thirty and thirty-five. Tall, good-looking, with black hair and fresh complexion. Educated Eton and the Sorbonne. Occupation: journalist—or so he called himself. Inclination: heroic, espouser of lost causes, champion of the minority. By nature: sentimental, a braggart, dishonest about most things except what he held to be fundamentally important: e.g. speed, poetry, religion, lost causes, the theatre, Beethoven, certain facets of the political tangle, more lost causes, food, drink, and children.

His attitude toward women, whom he fascinated, was unmoral. His opinion of them: that they had no finer feelings, merely appetites—for clothes, for love, for security, for childbearing.

On the debit side, thought Kevin, Stephen Cormac McFadden Lawlor did not balance the scales. He had made money in various unscrupulous ways: fiddling currency, evading taxes, selling other people's jewelry on commission in countries where the exchange shared a profit. Nothing really crooked; nothing perfectly straight. To him, such things did not matter. He would smuggle a diamond necklace through the Customs for an English dowager— loose in his pocket, generally—and then sit down and argue with rare passion about the terrible sanity, the honesty of John Clare; he would willingly sign a cheque for fifty pounds knowing that his bank could not honour it, and then he would spend an hour persuading a rich American to give a hundred dollars to the Pestalozzi International Settlement for War-displaced Children—and he would *post* the hundred dollars to Pestalozzi there and then.

In the case of Stephen Lawlor there was perhaps no credit and debit side, after all—only a mixture. He had charm, which he frequently used to obtain unsavoury ends; he had kindliness, but he could be unfeeling to the point of mania—particularly where women were concerned. He could concentrate every nerve and tissue of his being on some quite unselfish ploy, which to him seemed worth the effort, and yet he could drift meaninglessly when the effort was exhausted. Brilliant, unstable, loyal to some secret code of his own, untrustworthy.

Unpredictable.

John Kevin said, "Damn," out loud. He had arrived at the dead end of Stephen Lawlor: unpredictable. It was true, but it helped not at all.

During the war they had served together in the Navy, their paths crossing and recrossing. Stephen Lawlor was the one who was mentioned in dispatches—the one who

31

constantly fell foul of the police patrols. Stephen Lawlor it was who dived after the young seaman who went overboard one January day off Start Point; Stephen Lawlor it was who faced the court martial for refusing to obey an order. Unpredictable.

"Damnation," said John Kevin.

A particularly savage jolt shook him back to consciousness of his surroundings. He glanced up, scowling at the wild grandeur of Glenmalure; he was in no mood for landscape.

The road interested him, however. The surface might not be perfect, but on the other hand it was a *safe* road. Young Miss Celia Dillon had been perfectly right: Steve Lawlor, an instinctively splendid driver, would never have gone over the edge by accident.

They came at length to a corner where the thick, low wall was cleanly broken. Two hurdles patched the gap. Kevin stopped his driver, told him to find a place off the road where he could wait, and climbed out to inspect Stephen Lawlor's final earthly indiscretion.

Beyond the wall was a steep slope of rock, shale and scrubby grass stretching for perhaps ten yards. Beyond that—the softer green of the valley two hundred feet below.

Kevin wandered along the road until it bent around far enough for him to look back at the fatal corner. Yes, it was, beyond the shale, pure cliff—a sudden rampart between more gentle, heather-covered slopes. He climbed the wall and slithered down, clutching at bracken to steady himself. Now, far below, he could see the blackened, twisted mess of Steve Lawlor's car. Three men were examining it. One, without any doubt, was Inspector O'Connor;

another took photographs; the third fanned himself with his hat.

John Kevin sat down on the heather and watched them idly.

All right, he thought. Someone had wanted to kill Stephen Lawlor; what reason could that person have for also wanting to kill John Kevin? There was no doubt in his mind that the wrecked car in the valley and the lorry beneath the Erne Street Bridge were subtly connected. But, in heaven's name, what further connection could there be between two men who had seen each other for two short days in five years?

He noticed now that O'Connor and the two other men had finished their scrutiny of the wreckage. They stood in consultation for a time; then the Inspector waved his hand and a police car drew out of the shade of a clump of oaks. The men climbed in. The car moved away.

If O'Connor was returning to Dublin, Kevin reasoned, he would presumably take this road. It might be illuminating to have a word with him. He therefore clambered back to the wall, perched himself upon it, and waited. Further along, on the grass verge, the taxi driver slumbered at the wheel of his ramshackle vehicle, a sporting paper over his face. Cloud shadows slipped across distant Glenmalure in a magnificence of constantly changing colour. Kevin stared without seeing.

Presently he heard a car approaching; he had not been wrong, then. O'Connor saw him at once. The car came to a standstill beside the taxi and the small, but authoritative figure got out. They met in silence.

"Well?" said the policeman finally.

33

Kevin jerked his head towards the precipice. "What did you find?"

O'Connor planted his little legs firmly astride, put his hands on his hips and stared, gimlet-eyed, at the big, untidy, fair young man in his jeans and peajacket, bright hair ruffled into a crest, camera slung over his shoulder.

A fox terrier of a man, Kevin thought.

"I found a few things," O'Connor replied finally.

"It was no accident," said Kevin.

The policeman nodded.

"But how d'you make a strong, self-willed man drive himself over a cliff?"

"You kill him first," replied O'Connor grimly. "You take off the brake, put the car in gear, release the clutch, and stand clear."

Quite suddenly John Kevin was afraid. He had been angry, then excited; now a complete comprehension of how narrowly he had escaped death came creeping up out of the soles of his feet until he felt limp and sick all over. He shuddered.

O'Connor said, "It's the very divil; we don't know anything about the chap." He looked enquiring.

"All right," said Kevin, leaning for support against the wall. And, much to the Inspector's surprise, he rattled off the whole of his dossier on Stephen Cormac McFadden Lawlor just as it had presented itself to his mind in the taxi.

"Well!" said O'Connor when it was over. "That's certainly concise and complete; that fills in a lot of gaps." He nodded. "Unpredictable, eh? Yes, that just about sums it up. Thanks very much. Yes."

The recital seemed to have given him new life. He glanced up at the young man's face. "Anything else?"

"There's a girl. Did she see you?"

"No. When?"

"Early this morning."

"No. A girl, eh? She came to you?"

"She did. Dillon's the name. Celia Dillon. I don't think she knows much about him. She's pretty upset. Fond of him, I gathered." He was worried about Miss Dillon. That creeping fear had perhaps shown him his own vulnerability, so that suddenly he had more sympathy for hers. "Look here," he added, "if she hasn't come to you of her own accord, perhaps it would be better . . . Will you let me handle her?"

O'Connor half-closed his sharp eyes. In the sunshine the tweed of his suit smelt more strongly. He looked like an acute little farmer summing up a heifer at a show. "It's your own lookout," he said finally, "whether you talk to her or not; it's your own lookout whether or not you pass on to me what she says. I shall see her, naturally, in the course of my duty. You've no idea of her address?"

"After that," said John Kevin, angry again, "I wouldn't tell you if I did know it."

He had been meaning—even wanting—to pour out to this cocksure but reassuring man the story of what had happened to him in the deep shadow under the railway bridge. Now, pride and fury made it impossible. He glared.

The Inspector gave another of his curt nods. "I wouldn't be surprised," he said, "if you didn't get into trouble before you leave this country, Mr. John Kevin. You've a peach of a little temper there and no mistake." He turned towards his car, then back again. "By the bye, you won't be leaving Dublin yet awhile, will you? A man's been murdered, and the Law doesn't like that."

He stumped away with a sprightly spring to his step and slammed the door of his car. As it swept by, he nodded smartly to the angry young man leaning against the wall. Another grim, curt, infuriating nod.

Kevin wandered back to his taxi. O'Connor's slamming of the door had awakened the driver.

"The guard!" he said, surprised. "What're they doing here?"

Kevin regarded him thoughtfully. "Didn't you read in the papers about a chap driving himself over a cliff? That's where he did it."

"You don't say." The driver folded his own paper and put it in his pocket. "I never read the headlines meself— only the racing. Is it back to Dublin now?"

John Kevin again experienced that tingle of fear up his spine. In Dublin somebody he had never seen was waiting to kill him, for a reason he couldn't begin to guess. Suddenly he had no wish at all to return there.

But he said, "Yes. The Melbourne," and climbed into the back seat.

He wasn't used to being afraid, and he didn't like it.

## IV

THE FIRST PERSON he saw on entering the hotel was Miss Celia Dillon, sitting on the edge of a chair, doing her best to pull a good pair of gloves into small pieces. He saw her an instant before she saw him, and the misery on her fair, child's face pierced him. Then the surprising dark eyes—seeming so very dark against her golden-brown skin, framed by the pale bell of hair—met his. She stood up.

"Hullo," said Kevin. "I wonder if it's too late to get any lunch." He was afraid she was going to weep.

Instead, however, just as she opened her mouth to speak, the dark eyes moved from his and fixed on something beyond him. Intent. Bright. Her voice, after the eyes, was ordinary and absurd. "I've been waiting quite a while," she said. "I wondered where you'd got to. Don't move. Just talk to me. I'm not the only one that's been waiting for you. And for heaven's sake don't turn round."

He watched the eyes move as the object of their scrutiny crossed the entrance hall.

37

"He's gone to the telephones," she said. "What *is* all this?" Now her voice did tremble.

Kevin said, "Are you sure he was waiting for me?"

"Positive. He'd been sitting there almost as long as I had. He wasn't a very good actor; his jaw sort of sagged as soon as you came in."

"Good." Kevin slung his camera off his shoulder. "We'll have a picture of this chap, and then we'll find out what number he's been ringing. How shall I know him?"

"Dark-red tie," said the girl instantly. "Grey suit. Brown hat in his hand."

Kevin was glad to notice that emergency had robbed her voice of its tremulous note. They stood together, tensed, watching the entrance to the passage which led to the telephones. It seemed an eternity before Celia said, "There!" in a taut, furious voice.

The man came into the hall, saw the camera, stopped dumbfounded. The shutter clicked. The man took a pace towards them, his mouth working angrily. He was thin, rat-faced, sallow. Then, abruptly, he turned and practically ran from the hotel.

"That was neat," said the girl. "I hardly saw the camera myself."

"I'm used to it. I seldom let people know I'm taking them. Now for the telephone number."

But when they had finally inveigled the girl at the switchboard into disclosing the destination of the call, it proved singularly unhelpful.

"This," said an impatient voice, "is the public call box of the Maryland Milk Bar; if you want the manager . . ."

"We don't," said Kevin, and replaced the receiver.

38

Celia was all for going to the milk bar straight away, but the young man shook his head. "Nobody will have seen anything. The telephone will be in a passage, out of sight. No point in choosing it, otherwise."

They returned, chastened, to the hotel foyer. The dining room was closed. Kevin felt sick with hunger. They went into the lounge and found a sofa in a secluded corner.

"Tea for four," said Kevin to the waiter. And to Celia, when he had gone, "Three for me, one for you. I'm famished."

After a pause she said, "Well?"

"Well what?"

Her eyes were very bright now. "Do you still think Steve drove himself over that cliff by mistake?"

"No, I don't. He couldn't have done so. It wasn't even on a corner."

She nodded. "So?"

"Two things, as I see it. . . . Either somebody tampered with his steering, or somebody pushed him over—as it were."

The girl glanced away abruptly. "No," she said, "I shan't cry again; I don't often." After a time she turned back. "But who? *Why?*"

Kevin sighed.

When she had poured out tea, and speaking between mouthfuls, he said, "Now, listen to me. See if you can make sense of this.

"Five years ago Steve Lawlor and I knew each other fairly well. We were both working in London at the time —he for an arty political magazine which went broke, and I for one of the national dailies. Then I got offered a job in

South America and Steve went off to Palestine. Since then we'd seen each other once—for forty-eight hours in Paris. Nothing unusual happened there. Nothing whatsoever.

"Now someone has killed Steve—well, he may have had plenty of enemies; he wasn't very careful of people's feelings. And someone—I'm damn sure it was the same person, too—has tried to kill me."

"Oh, *no!*" The girl turned, eyes wide.

He told her of what had happened under the railway bridge in Erne Street.

Surprisingly—he was beginning to find her rather a surprising person—she became collected and determined at this fresh news.

"The first thing you're going to do," she said, "is to get out of those clothes and this hotel. Somebody dressed like you are, in Dublin, in the Melbourne— Why, you're a sitting target. Surely you can see that?"

"Yes, I suppose I am."

"There are lots of small hotels—or maybe a boarding house. And you'll have to try and look less fantastic."

He blinked.

"A bit more like other people. It won't be easy with that hair."

"I'm not dyeing it," said Kevin firmly, seeing a glint in her eye.

She giggled. She was, he thought, very young in some ways. But definitely not in others. There was sense in what she had said. He liked the idea of a small secluded boarding house with a large, fierce, Irish proprietress; it made him feel safer to think of it.

40

"Of course," said Celia Dillon, not looking at him, "you *could* go back to England."

"Oh, no, I couldn't. The guard would have something to say about that. Besides, I don't want to. I'm curious by nature; I'll never rest if I don't find out what's behind this crazy business."

Celia turned and stared at him. Quite suddenly he had become a person in his own right—not an adjunct of Stephen Lawlor's rich personality. She stared hard at his brown face, and found it disturbing. He looked—with his very short, curling hair, so startlingly fair, and his grey, straight eyes—more solid than he really was. He looked a simple person: open, foursquare and direct. But he wasn't like that at all; his personality was slender, lean, perhaps too sensitive. Staring at him she now caught nuances of it in his face. When he smiled he no longer looked foursquare and solid, but a trifle shy, undefended, a dreamer.

"You need looking after," she said, "or you'll get yourself hurt."

"That seems likely."

She brooded for a while, delicate chin cupped in hand. Then she said, "I know you think I'm a booby, but I was in love with Steve. I—I think he loved me, too—a bit."

He would have made you think so, anyway, Kevin thought.

"I know men didn't awfully like him," she went on, "but he was so— Oh, I don't know. Warm, generous, exciting to be with."

"He was."

"You agree?" She was staggered.

41

"Yes, I do. He was other things as well, but no matter. Go on."

"He was up to something," she said—for the second time. "He— He was—" She beat the arm of the sofa with her fist. "I can't explain; he was sort of—*excited* about something. Impatient. Oh, it doesn't make sense. The atmosphere was all wrong; it didn't add up."

"Yes, I think it did. Can't you be more particular? Facts?"

She studied him for a time in silence.

"Why didn't you go to the police this morning?" he asked lightly.

She traced the pattern of the carpet with her toe. Then she said, "You're awfully acute really, aren't you? I mean you look sort of—vague and hearty, but you don't miss a thing."

"Why didn't you go to the guard?"

"Because— Because, you see, I'm pretty certain Steve was up to no good. And I—I loved him. And now that he's dead—" She choked, and the old misery returned.

"Why," demanded Kevin, relentless, "do you think he was up to no good? Hadn't you better tell me what you know?"

But she knew very little; it was a matter of atmosphere more than of fact, yet he felt he could trust her intuition. Women, he knew, talk a lot of this virtue (if it be such) but not always in terms of nonsense. There had been telephone calls, for instance, when he and she had been dining together. Why telephone calls, she demanded, since he knew no one in Ireland—or so he said? Or if, in fact, he did know people in Ireland, why say that he didn't?

Could they all have been trunk calls from England or from Paris? They could, but was that likely?

As she spoke, haltingly, feeling for this atmosphere of deceit which defied fact, Kevin could share her mood and her disquiet. It was likely, he thought as he listened, that Stephen Lawlor had been "up to something." But what? And how had it brought about his death? And where in the devil's name did he, John Kevin, enter into it? What did he share with the dead man? What had he seen, or heard, which called for the long silence of death lest he should tell it? For that surely was the answer.

And then, again, he saw in his mind's eye the orange board over the doorway of the house on the quay: the Tara Lounge. Something he had heard or seen . . . No, it was absurd. His head was beginning to spin with so many unanswered, unanswerable questions.

He said, "By the way, where did Steve live—if he wasn't staying with his aunt out at Drumnagh?"

"He had a flat. Not his. It belongs to a friend of mine, Tony Grant—a cousin, actually. When I met Steve in London, and he said he was coming to Ireland, he asked me to look out for a place for him. And I thought of Tony, you see. He lent it to Steve. Nice of him, really."

So Stephen Lawlor, with an aunt waiting to see him in Drumnagh, a mere thirty miles from the city, and any number of hotels at his disposal, must have a flat of his own. A private place. Why?

"Can we get in?" he said. "I'd like to have a look at it."

"Well—I don't know how. Unless we burgle it. There was only one key, and I suppose the guard have got that now."

"Yes, I suppose they have." He felt, at that moment, suddenly weary of the whole drama. It was too absurd. And he wanted to roam the grey streets and the squares with his camera, his love.

The girl seemed to sense this. "Come on," she said. "Let's get your bag and move you somewhere a bit less ostentatious."

He obeyed blankly. They went out of the lounge, to the lift, and up to the third floor.

It did not strike him immediately; his mind was on other things, dreaming a little (as she had suspected) of Georgian vistas, wrought iron, pilasters, caryatids, pediments, and the gentle afternoon sunshine gracing them all. He stood, in this pleasance, staring at his dressing table without seeing it. He remembered how the light, looking eastward down the Liffey in the morning, had glowed with the quiet, yet somehow brilliant lustre of a pearl. The masts and cranes and warehouses gleaming with an almost Venetian radiance . . .

Then he saw that the box containing a new roll of film, which lay on the dressing table, had been opened. It was an infinitesimal detail, yet he noticed it. The label had been broken. He said, "Someone's been in this room."

"The maid," said Celia, but her voice was not quite steady.

Kevin lifted the box, opened it, slid out the roll. It had been exposed.

"Someone's been in here," he said again. He began to notice other small details. The suitcase which he had left

44

unlatched was now neatly closed. It *could* have been the maid, no doubt, but the exposed film . . .

"Ugh," said the girl, shuddering. "I don't like this. I'm scared. You'd better go back to England."

"Not on your life."

She went to his private bathroom and opened the door. "Where's the light?" she said; and he, lost in speculation, not awake to danger yet, answered, "Outside— in the best interests of safety." He heard the click of the switch, and an exclamation of dismay.

"It doesn't work."

Then his brain functioned. He swung around and shouted, "Come here. Come here this instant."

Astonished, she halted on the threshold and obeyed him, noticing how strained, how pale beneath the tan his face had suddenly become.

He switched on the reading lamp beside the bed and, the cord trailing, advanced with it into the bathroom, pushing her aside. It didn't take a moment to discover why the light wasn't working. It was wired to the chromium handle of the door. Anyone who had known that the switch was outside the room would have pressed it before going it—would have pressed it, most likely, with one hand on the doorknob.

Moreover, he discovered a moment later, the switch had been tampered with also; it wouldn't cut the current.

He turned and stared at the girl, and she stared at him. Owlishly. In silence.

_____ 

CELIA's Uncle Edward Dillon sat upright
in a tall wing-backed armchair, a Waterford sherry glass
pressed against the tip of his nose, which was long, straight
and pointed like the rest of him. Both in mind and body
Celia's Uncle Edward Dillon was long, straight and pointed.
His grey eyes were quite black and very bright like two
black currants with dew on them. His face was parchment-
coloured and all perpendicular lines; he had not even any
lateral eyebrows to mar the perpendiculars of his face. Instead there was a slanting tuft on each side of the bridge
of his nose which gave him a devilish air. His forehead was
lofty and his grey, sparse hair started right on top of his
head.

Watching him, Kevin thought that the Devil might
well look thus. Intelligent, bright-eyed, urbane, rather
weary, attired in a dark-red velvet smoking jacket, with a
Waterford sherry glass pressed to his nose. Excellent
sherry in the glass, too. And an excellent Chippendale
chair on which to sit.

46

Uncle Edward Dillon said, "Um," and regarded the two young people wisely.

Kevin said, "I know it must sound quite fantastic to you, but . . ."

"I once *met* Stephen Lawlor," said Uncle Edward gently. "Moreover, I've known his Aunt Bella for years. Everything connected with that family is fantastic."

"You do see," said Celia, wandering about the room in an irritating way, touching things. "You do see that he can't possibly stay in a hotel. Anything might happen."

"I see that, yes. I am not, however, altogether delighted at the idea of my establishment being turned into a fort or blockhouse." The black eyes glittered, belying the words.

"No?" said his niece absently. "Heavens, it wouldn't be the first time. Look at the way you behaved in the Troubles."

"The Troubles," said Uncle Edward, "were a matter of my artistic conscience. This sounds to me like political strife—OGPU, Maffia, Gestapo." He shuddered delicately, and finished his sherry. "But quite fascinating, I agree. Finian will be delighted."

"Finian," Celia explained, "is Uncle's valet . . ."

"Butler, if you please. Or maybe bodyguard. It is not certain just how many Englishmen he murdered in the Troubles. Many, I imagine."

Kevin said, "I'm English."

"Your name, however, and the fact that you are a persecuted man, will redeem you in Finian's eyes. Anyway, he would as soon have murdered Chinamen or Danes; he is a remarkably impartial man." He refilled Kevin's glass and then his own. "Tell me, you surely made enquiries at the

47

hotel as to whether anyone had been admitted to your room?"

"That was simple. The maid knew all about it; she said that she'd let the electrician in only a short while before."

"He told her," Celia added, "that he had orders to repair the light over the mirror in the bathroom."

Uncle Edward pursed his lips. "And *was* it the hotel electrician?"

"Oh, no, of course not; he said he was new to the job."

"He stood a good chance of electrocuting the maid instead of you."

"No. When he'd done his dirty work he found her again—there's only one on duty in the afternoons—and told her that the gentleman in 302 had come in and didn't want to be disturbed."

"Well-planned."

"He knew," concluded Kevin grimly, "just what he was up to."

"You reported it to the management, of course?"

"No. I simply disconnected the contraption."

"Why didn't you report it?"

"Because it would have started a hue and cry; because I wouldn't be surprised if your precious guard don't already think I'm implicated in Steve Lawlor's death."

Uncle Edward, after a pause, said, "It was not a *certain* way to account for you, all the same." He tapped his fingertips together. "I find it unpleasantly casual. The maid *might* have been killed—or a page boy, or the hotel manager . . ."

"Or me," said Celia faintly.

After a tiny pause he added, "Or you, my dear. Exactly.

It points to a very catholic indiscrimination. I don't think this is the last attempt."

There was silence in the gracious room.

"No," said Kevin. "Neither do I."

"But *why?*" cried the girl suddenly. "Can't you think of any reason at all?"

"No. None." He shook his head, bemused. "Absolutely none."

Edward Dillon sipped his sherry. "You are quite obviously in possession of knowledge which is dangerous—highly dangerous to some other person, or possibly to a group of persons."

Kevin stood up and walked away from them to one of the tall windows at the end of the room. He could not bring himself to tell them of that strange sense of foreboding which had struck him when he looked at the name *Tara Lounge* written in black on an orange board above the door of a shabby bar. It was too absurd, too personal, and, from the alcoholic point of view, too squalid. Perhaps when he had returned there and spoken to this Shaun O'Farrell, the guardian of his drunken lapse, he would know more, and be able to speak. But now . . .

"I know of no reason," he said, his voice tight with impotent anger. "None, none, none. That's what's so maddening. But I'm sure the key to it is Stephen Lawlor. I've no enemies."

"He would have had dozens, I imagine," said Edward Dillon dryly.

"Uncle! How dare you . . ."

"Celia, my child, you are in no position to judge the character of Mr. Lawlor. You were, and still are, bemused and bewildered by all that charm and good looks. A most bewitching lover, I've no doubt. Let us leave it at that."

He looked at John Kevin and his eyes glittered.

The young man said, "I must get into this flat, the one Tony Grant lent him."

"Wouldn't it be better," suggested the old man, "to go to the guard and put it all in their hands?"

"No," snapped Celia, thinking of the honour (or lack of it) of her lovely Stephen.

"No," said Kevin, more hesitantly. "Not yet, anyway. I—I'd like to know more, just a little more before I do that. Besides—" He thought, with irritation, of Inspector O'Connor's curt little nod—half warming, half sardonic mirth—as he swept by in his car.

"No, not yet," he concluded, almost with defiance. "I want to pay a visit to the flat, and I want to talk to—to a man I met last night. Then maybe I'll go to the guard."

He looked very obstinate, standing in the middle of that graceful room, still wearing his ancient jeans and jacket. He looked, Celia thought, much in need of protection. Foolish but endearing.

Uncle Edward Dillon said, "You know, I can't help liking the English. Funny thing."

Finian Colm Francisco Hogan was not quite what Kevin had expected. He was tall and slight, with the long head on an El Greco "extra": one of the soldiers, maybe, in a crucifixion, or one of the minor courtiers in a palace. His grandmother had been Spanish; hence the Francisco. He possessed a strange calm and a dignity which made it easier

50

to envisage him as butler than as bodyguard. This was
doubtless the Spaniard in his blood. There was also, as
Kevin was to discover later, a whole tribe of Hogan, Han-
nigan, O'Leary, Byrne and Maguire corpuscles flooding
through his veins. The mixture, when roused, was spectacular.

Now, however, all was calm and dignified.

"Sure," said Finian, "I know the Tara—Lounge, as they
call it—and it's a mean sort of a place, and no place at all for
a gentleman, if you'll excuse me saying so, sor. Now
what's to prevent me going there and finding this Shaun
O'Farrell and bringing him to some other bar where there
aren't a lot of clumsy louts with no shine on their boots
listening to every word you say? How would that be
now?"

From many points of view this seemed a good suggestion.

"As to Mr. Tony Grant's place of residence—" Finian
arched one black, sardonic eyebrow. "That won't present
many difficulties. I've visited there a couple of times meself, since Mr. Tony is related, you know, him being me
lord and master's nephew. Me late mistress was a Grant,
God rest her soul."

It was evident to Kevin that all he could do now was
to place himself entirely in Finian's long, capable hands.
(The hands, he noticed again, the almost absurdly attenu-
ated hands of an El Greco.)

And so, at a quarter past eight, suitably dressed in a dark
suit and macintosh, with a hat concealing most of his hair,
he sat decorously over a glass of Guinness in a secluded
alcove in what Finian had assured him was a dull and re-
spectable "lounge." In common with many Dublin bars

51

the impression was of a waiting room in a large provincial railway station. The clientele were forever attending some long overdue train, the arrival of which was hardly a probability any more.

At eight-thirty Finian came into this place, leading a shabby, but cheery-looking fellow whose features raised not the slightest tremor of recognition in Kevin's brain. It was only now, faced with this drinking companion of not yet twenty-four hours past, that he realized how regrettably, humiliatingly drunk he must have been.

Mr. Shaun O'Farrell sat down at his table, accepted a Guinness, and stared with humorous, but rheumy eyes. He smelled strongly of onions.

"Ah," he said, "well, I'm not surprised you don't recognize me, for it was a dirty trick of Tom Milligan to serve you that rotten, good-for-nothing lousy firewater under the fine name of whisky. If I'd known what he was doing I'd have punched his nose on your behalf, so cross me heart I would."

"So it wasn't proper whisky?"

"No, my dear soul, it was not. If you ask my opinion he brews it up himself in his own bathtub."

Kevin was relieved somewhat. Tom Milligan's home brew explained very clearly the lost hours of his night's carousal. He knew that his head was strong enough to take any normal drink.

"As I said," remarked Finian in a lofty way, "it's no place for you to have been, that Tara Lounge."

"No place at all," agreed Mr. O'Farrell cheerfully. "And I said to meself, I said, 'Now if you don't look after that fellow, Shaun, me boy, there'll be broken heads and lost wallets in this bar before they turn out the lights.' "

"I'm very obliged to you, I'm sure," muttered Kevin, feeling a fool under Finian's Olympian disdain. "But what I want to know—and it's very important that you should try and remember—is this—" He moistened his lips and, despite the intensification of the smell of onions, leaned forward. "Did I—did I seem to see anybody or anything —did I hear anything, or speak to anybody, or find anything . . . Was there any incident at all while you were with me that seemed to—to impress me, or excite me?"

Shaun O'Farrell pushed back his battered hat and scratched his head. For some time he searched his memory in silence.

"Well," he said at last, "everything seemed to excite you, boy. I mean there wasn't a grain of sense in anything you did or said. And why should there be after four glasses of . . ."

"Yes, yes. But you can't recall any particular detail?"

The blankness of the man's face gave Kevin his answer. There was no more to be said. Mr. O'Farrell vanished into the night a pound richer, and Kevin, attended by Finian in a majestic mood, found himself no whit wiser.

For a time he sat in silence staring at his Guinness. Perhaps the dejection of his bearing softened Finian's heart. He said, "Come now, it's not as bad as all that, surely. Supposing we go and take a look at the inside of Mr. Tony Grant's place." Clearly he was looking forward to this part of the evening; a kind of relish crept into his voice at the mention of it.

Kevin, glancing up at him, could not help smiling. "How much do you know about all this?" he asked.

53

Finian looked more majestic than ever. "As much as Mr. Edward Dillon thought fit to tell me," he replied with hauteur. "And that's enough for me. He said you were in danger and I was to look after you. He said that whether I broke the law or not was me own lookout, as it always has been; but if I got in trouble—with the guard, he said— I wasn't to mention his good name at all or he'd disown me entirely and abandon me to me fate. Not that he meant it, mind you, for if I wasn't there to look after him he'd be as helpless as a newborn babe without his mother."

Kevin sighed. "You know almost as much as I do. I *am* in danger, and in some way it's connected with Mr. Stephen Lawlor's death. Beyond that—" He shrugged.

"Mr. Lawlor," said Finian, "was a fine, swaggering buckaroo to turn any girl's heart; but he was no boy for our Miss Celia and I'm not sorry he's out of her reach, God rest his soul, all the same."

"Does she live with her uncle, by the way?"

"Except when she's with her old father—Mr. Edward's brother—at Denisstown, and that's way out the back-o'-beyond in County Clare. A depressing lump of a place situated in a bog."

That part of Finian Colm Francisco Hogan which was not Spanish was clearly Dublin to the core.

"And now, sor," he said, "if you're ready, it's a handy sort of twilight this very moment—just right for getting in and out of places without being seen."

The flat which Stephen Lawlor had been lent by Celia's cousin was apparently one of twelve in a block consisting of three Georgian houses thrown together and modernized.

While Kevin waited at the corner, Finian interviewed the caretaker, whom he knew well and on whose racing tips he apparently won money with regularity.

It was a cool damp evening, rain threatening, and the light was murky, indistinct under heavy cloud. The houses lay in a backwater square, very silent except for fluttering leaves and an occasional car. The street lamps, through the leaves, cast wavering shadows. Kevin found himself standing with his back against the wall; it was by now an automatic attitude. He was continually conscious of a shudder in the small of his spine which he recognized as the hallmark of the hunted. He didn't like it at all, and he was relieved to see his bodyguard once again.

Finian was pleased. The guard, he said, had kept a man watching the flat all day; but they had now withdrawn, and the caretaker was in charge—a stupid old fellow, Finian pronounced, except in the matter of horseflesh. He led the way cautiously round to the back of the houses, where a narrow lane, flanked on either side by walls, ran parallel with the main street.

"Gardens," Finian explained. "The only tricky part is getting over here. After that it'll be as easy as picking daisies."

The noise they made in climbing the wall seemed enough to waken not only caretakers but the dead. Finian, lifted by Kevin, managed to grab the parapet at the third attempt and scrabbled his way, snorting, to the top. He then jumped onto what sounded like a pile of dry sticks. Presently, after an eternity—or so it seemed to Kevin, wait-

55

ing breathlessly in the lane—a piece of rope slithered over the wall and dangled to his feet. He seized it, hoping that Finian was holding firm on the other side, and hauled himself up and over, making, if possible, more noise than his confederate had.

Together they crouched in the shadow of a lilac bush, and waited. The leaves fluttered; a cat serenaded in the distance; a clock struck. The house before them was dark and silent, except for two lighted windows on the top floor. One was half-open, and from it issued the clear bittersweet theme of the slow movement from the *Emperor Concerto*.

"Mr. Grant has the first floor," whispered Finian. "Couldn't be easier, could it now?"

He was right. A wrought-iron staircase, overhung with jasmine, led from the garden to a Regency balcony running the entire length of the floor. They made their way cautiously towards it. A white cat fled at their approach. Above them the orchestra rose to Beethoven's climax and subsided.

The staircase creaked agonizingly as they mounted it, but once under the canopy of the verandah, jasmine hanging in loops and festoons about them, they were perfectly screened and safe.

Finian produced a jar from his pocket, opened it, and examined the tall window with a professional eye. He then smeared what appeared to be treacle all over the pane, spread a piece of brown paper neatly across the sticky mess, smoothed it, and struck it neatly with his fist. When he drew the paper away, much of the pane came with it.

He put his hand through the jagged hole thus left and slipped the catch of the window. It opened soundlessly.

"Now," he said, "in you go and do whatever you want to do. I'll keep watch right here. Don't be longer than you need, and draw the curtains behind you."

Kevin, aware once more of that flicker of nerves in the small of his back, stepped into the thick, unknown darkness of the house.

By the light of his torch he could see that he was in a sitting room. On the far side of it was the doorway to a small hall. He shut this door, drew the curtains and switched on a reading lamp, first spreading across the shade a large red handkerchief which Finian had supplied for the purpose. Then he began to examine the room. It did not take him long to find that there was little of Stephen Lawlor here; he had, after all, inhabited the place for a mere ten days. The bedroom would probably prove more rewarding.

He switched off the light, took the handkerchief and went into the hall. There were two doors apart from that through which he had just come; one led to the kitchen, the other to a surprisingly large bedroom. He put the handkerchief over the bedside lamp and switched it on.

Yes, here there were signs of Lawlor. The books by the bed: *Poems of John Clare*, *Shakespeare's Sonnets*, two novels and *The Anatomy of Melancholy*. Draped over the mirror of the dressing table was the tie, interlinking chains in black and grey on white, which they had bought, laughing together, in the Rue de la Paix. He recognized the stud box on the chest of drawers and opened it idly—he was far from sure, in any case, of what he expected to find. Beneath the studs and collar buttons his finger disclosed a silver badge; he frowned over it—over the fasces. Had Steve been a Fascist then? Of course, many of his generation, for the hell of it, had joined the British League, Moseley's bright boys. It was surprising all the same. In the top right-hand drawer he found, among letters, a strange document advertising lewd film shows in Marseilles; a programme for *Fidelio* at the Paris Opera; a pamphlet calling upon free men the world over to join the United Freedom Movement; a receipt for a cheque, fifty pounds, which Mr. Lawlor had sent to some Home of Mercy run by Catholics for the slum children of Dijon.

Lewd films in Marseilles, United Freedom in London, *Fidelio* in Paris, slum children in Dijon: yes, they were outward signs of the cipher which had been Stephen Lawlor. Kevin found them revealing, yet blank. He found the Fascist badge revealing, yet blank also.

What did he hope to discover, anyway? He hardly knew. Something, perhaps, to jog a memory—a key to the Tara Lounge; a clue to that piece of cord dangling, so idle, yet so lethal, from the electric-light socket to the doorknob; a word to make plain the cipher which had been Stephen Lawlor.

He returned to the bed and slid open the drawer of the bedside table. At the back of it, reposing innocently on empty aspirin bottles and pencil ends, lay a small, red book which he recognized instantly: it was Steve Lawlor's diary. He had just picked it up when he heard the terrifying and unmistakable sound of a latchkey being gently inserted into the front door of the flat.

His blood froze. For all eternity he stood there, helpless; then, in one, almost instinctive movement, he shut the little drawer, flicked off the light, grabbed the handkerchief and flattened himself against the wall. Almost at the same moment the front door closed with a click, and there was silence. Someone was undoubtedly inside the flat with him. Who? There was only one key, Celia had said. They had agreed that Inspector O'Connor must hold this key. Therefore the man in the hall must be a policeman.

Kevin's brain worked very quickly and clearly now.

They had only *guessed* that the key would be found by the police in Stephen Lawlor's pocket. If it had not been there, then the person in possession of it—the only person who could be in possession of it—was Stephen Lawlor's murderer.

Kevin could hear nothing now but the panic pounding of his own heart. Absolute, dead, waiting silence. The police, he reasoned, would not enter like this—so quietly, without turning on a light. Then the alternative . . .

Damnation! It was the unknown that frightened him. And if the man who stood now in the hall had killed Stephen, might he not be the same man who had tried twice to kill John Kevin? Or could it have been the caretaker, just opening the door, peering in, and closing it again?

For hours, for days, it seemed, he stood there, back to the wall, listening to the pounding of his heart. He wanted Finian badly, but Finian lay through the hall. Alternatively he wanted some means of protection—a revolver at best, a poker at worst.

Perhaps, after all—since the leaden silence continued minute after minute, hour after hour, day after day—it had merely been the caretaker on his round. Perhaps, after all . . .

He froze again. Someone was opening the bedroom door: he heard the soft whisper of the door brushing the carpet.

And then, blindingly, a torch flashed on, swept around the room and fixed its beam dead in his eyes. He was impaled, helpless, on that spear of cruel light.

The man behind the torch grunted—it was nearly a laugh —and then, surprisingly, swung the beam up into his own face so that John Kevin might see it.

Kevin's breath caught in his throat, and he fell back against the wall, cracking his head quite painfully.

For the man confronting him was neither a policeman nor Stephen Lawlor's murderer. It was Stephen Lawlor himself, smiling.

*part two:* **UNEASY SLEEP**

"The thing to do," said Stephen Lawlor, long before Kevin had found breath to speak, "would be to call off your watchdog, and then we could talk without fear of being garrotted."

Kevin moistened his lips and said, "But, Steve . . ."

"Look. Don't ask questions—not now and here. Get rid of the trusty Finian and then we'll go somewhere less grisly."

"It—won't be so easy to get rid of Finian; he's been told not to let me out of his sight."

"That's understandable. You always have needed looking after. Are you staying with old Edward Dillon?"

"Yes." Kevin caught, in the half-light cast by the torch, a shadow of the old Lawlor grin.

A shadow of the old Lawlor voice said, "You certainly get around, don't you?" But he could see now, or perhaps he could sense, how brittle with nerves and weariness this man was.

"All right," said Lawlor. "Do this. Go back to old Dillon's place with the watchdog, let him tuck you safely in bed, then slip out again, turn left as you leave the house and meet me on the corner."

"By the pillar box?"

"That's the one. And," said Stephen Lawlor, his voice suddenly sharp with his own secret thoughts, "for heaven's sake don't keep me hanging around long. I needn't explain why."

Kevin nodded and made for the door, his brain literally in a state of suspension. It had only needed this final unreality—Stephen Lawlor alive—to make the nightmare complete.

"By the way," said that taut, weary voice in the darkness, "I didn't ask exactly what you were doing here. Enquiring into the cause of my—my death, no doubt?"

"Yes. I was."

"You haven't—you haven't been collecting clues, have you? I mean, you haven't removed anything?"

John Kevin's fingers closed around the diary in his pocket, and, guided by some intuition he could not explain, he said, "No."

An hour later they sat opposite each other in an alcove at the Green Cockatoo. This all-night eating house appeared to have collected all that was bizarre and unaccountable in Dublin. There were a great many chattering young men, dressed in crew-neck sweaters or in checked shirts; there were a few prostitutes, since it was raining outside in O'Connell Street; there were many couples with heads close together, intent on their own secrets. The atmosphere was thick with cigarette smoke under a low ceiling, and it was very hot and airless.

Stephen Lawlor wore glasses; the lenses were grotesque, now magnifying, now dissipating his eyes as he moved. Otherwise he looked exactly the same as when Kevin had seen him in Paris, except that he was nervous—not nervous in fear, it seemed to Kevin, but nervous with excitement.

"I'm surprised," Kevin said, "that you dare come to a place like this—crowded."

Lawlor nodded over his coffeecup. "It seems odd," he agreed, "and yet, you see, I am dead—no one expects to see me, either here or anywhere else. Add the fact that I know nobody in Dublin—except, of course, those who think me *kaput*. Besides, these—" And he touched the spectacles.

He was right. They changed his features in a quite inexplicable way—broadening his long, handsome face and casting an angle of sharp light onto his cheekbones, flattening them.

They were silent for a while. Then Kevin said, "Well?"

The other smiled faintly, his dark eyes suddenly intense behind the fantastic spectacles. "Yes," he said. "I—I hardly know where to start."

"You could do worse," said Kevin, "than explain, since you aren't dead, who exactly is. And how did he come about your watch, suit, socks, shoes, shirt, tie, and signet ring? And your birthmark."

Lawlor nodded. When he leaned forward he had a pronounced widow's peak. Women, Kevin knew, found it irresistible; they found the very dark, curling hair irresistible, too. Kevin was not so affected. He felt angry now, and again he said, "Well?"

"I don't know who the fellow was," Lawlor admitted. His voice faltered, and suddenly he dropped his head into his hands. It was a movement of such dejection that John Kevin, angry though he was, could not repress a twinge of pity.

After a time he looked up. "I'll tell you as best I can, John. God alone knows whether you'll believe it, but it's true. Mad, but true." He poured himself out more black coffee.

"Somebody killed that fellow, thinking it was me. I got back to the flat last night—it seems about a week ago now —and there he was, lying in the sitting room with his head bashed in." He shuddered. "God in heaven, what a shock that was."

"But why?" demanded Kevin. "Why should anybody want to kill you? What have you been up to?"

Lawlor pursed his lips. "There's a good enough reason," he said. "I don't *know* it's the reason, but it easily might be."

"Go on."

"Well, you know what I am. Just before I left Paris, about twelve days ago now, a fellow came up to me—I was sitting outside Jean-Pierre's with a *fine*—and said that he understood I was pretty expert at evading the Customs people. Naturally, I was a bit put out; I asked him where in hell he got such an idea from.

"He gave that one a miss, and turned on a good deal of charm—he was an Englishman, by the way—and stood me a couple more *fines*, and generally gave me to understand that he was a perfectly trustworthy fellow—in an *un*trustworthy sort of way." He smiled faintly. "I mean he mentioned one or two of the boys quite casually in his conversation: Maxim, and Joey Lachette, and Raôul—oh, and several others. I don't quite know whether he thought I was one of them or not. At any rate, he'd obviously heard about me arriving from London with old Lady P.'s diamond whatnot in my pocket. Seems everybody in Paris knows that one.

"I didn't tell him a thing—just let him think what he liked. If he wanted to believe I was a crook, he could do so as far as I was concerned; he wasn't the first, and anyway I was a bit hard up for cash.

"Well, he had something he wanted taken to Dublin, to cut a long story short. It was a sealed package, he said, looking like the cat that'd eaten the canary. I said I didn't give a hoot in hell what was *in* his precious package so long as he paid me well. I was feeling a bit high by that time, and I was mad because it seemed everyone on the Left Bank knew about me and Lady P.'s trinkets. Also, as I say, I was short of cash. So I said I'd take his package, and what was he going to fork out? And bless my soul, John, if he didn't say two hundred quid."

Kevin whistled quietly.

"Exactly. Well, your guess is as good as mine, but I'd say dope. It wasn't a big packet, but it weighed pretty heavy."

"Go on."

"All right. So I agreed to bring it over. He gave me an address here, and I was to deliver it the same evening that I arrived. So far, so good. I came by air, by the way. Did you?"

"Yes."

"Good. Then you know what happens at Dublin air-

67

port. They usher you into that sort of lounge place to wait your turn at the Customs. Remember?"

"Yes."

"And between the lounge and the Customs there's a short passageway and a glass partition?"

"Yes, there is."

"Well, now, I had this 'sealed package' in the pocket of my raincoat, and the coat was over my arm. I always find that's the best place, for various reasons, as it happens. And this time, my old Johnno, I was right. I looked through the glass partition and damn me if the whole Customs department wasn't buzzing with civic guard—flatfooted coppers left, right and centre."

"You got rid of the parcel?"

"Too damn sure I did. I slipped it out of the coat pocket, put it on the floor under my seat—I was sitting on one of those banquette things along the wall—and gave it a neat little kick." He grinned suddenly at the memory. "It landed under an old granny with half a dozen kids hanging onto her." The grin faded as abruptly as it had come. "I may as well add that my payment for these services was in two parts—a hundred in Paris, in advance, and a hundred on delivery."

He frowned, looking Kevin directly in the eye. "You know," he said, "I don't think I'm really dishonest, John. Do you?"

Kevin grinned. "I daresay it's relative like most other things. Go on."

"Well, I say that because the first thing I did, when I'd got safely through the Customs and into the city, was to

68

go to the address the chap in Paris had given me and own up."

Kevin was surprised.

"Yes, I did. I mean, it seemed the only thing to do. The chap was a perfect rat, and I loathed him on sight. When I told him what had happened he went berserk; he said I'd pay for it, and all the rest of the twaddle. I said I was damn sorry, but I wasn't going to the jug just because someone was too lazy to trot their own dope about the place."

"That," said Kevin, "wasn't very clever of you."

"No, it wasn't. But I was mad."

"What then?"

"Oh, then he went very quiet and nasty. He wanted to know how I'd found out it was dope."

"Naturally," said Kevin.

"Well, it was obvious. I told him so. 'Plain as the nose on your face,' I said—and that made him crazy again."

"So?"

"So finally we parted on the very worst of terms. The dope was found eventually, of course, but it couldn't be pinned on anybody." He mused for a time in silence, peering into his coffeecup. "I reckon that little parcel was worth about seven thousand or more, John, depending on what sort it was. Frankly I was damn glad the police had found it. I don't like the dope business; it's too damn dirty."

Kevin repressed a smile. How like Steve Lawlor that was—the mixture of moralities.

"Well, then," Lawlor continued. "All was quiet and friendly for about three days. Then someone tried to push me under a lorry."

Kevin sat up sharply. "The devil they did!"

"Yes. I didn't like it. Of course, as you say, I should never have let out my shot in the dark about the parcel containing dope; it was that, not losing the thing, which made me dangerous. However, it didn't work; it's a damn clumsy way to finish someone off, in any case. Heaven alone knows how I missed the lorry, but I did. Of course it was impossible to tell who'd done it; quite a crowd collected straight away.

"After that I got jumpy." He glanced up. "I daresay Celia told you I was jumpy."

"She did, yes."

"Well, I was. So would you be."

"Go on."

"Can't you guess?"

"Only in parts."

Lawlor sighed deeply and ran a hand through his hair.

"Nothing else happened until yesterday evening, and I'm not too sure what happened then."

"You mean this body in your flat."

Lawlor nodded. "The only thing I can imagine is that he was a friend of Celia's cousin, Tony Grant; come to borrow a book, maybe, or just to pay a visit. Grant's in America, but I daresay all his friends don't know that.

"This fellow was about my size—same kind of hair, too. Obviously he'd been standing with his back to the window. Someone had come in the way you did this evening; they saw what they thought was me, and let fly. Wham!" He gesticulated. His face was quite bleak now—unutterably weary. For what seemed a long, long time he was silent. Finally without looking up, he said, "I—I can't expect you to be anything but horrified by what I did then. I'm horri-

70

fied myself, come to that." He looked up, intensely serious now, his features drawn and taut. "It's no fun being hunted, John," he said. "I was all to bits. Every footstep behind me made my blood run cold; if a car backfired in the street I nearly had a heart attack. And I reckoned that if they thought they'd killed me they might as well go on thinking it. Besides— Well, to be frank, I couldn't afford to be faced with a body in my sitting room; it would mean a lot of enquiries—and my behaviour this last year or two couldn't stand much enquiry."

"I think," said Kevin grimly, "I understand."

Lawlor smiled briefly—a glimmer of the old warmth, quickly dying. "You're a good chum, John. Always have been."

"You faked him up to look like you."

"Yes. I . . . Oh, God, it was ghastly. You see, it wasn't only a question of 'faking,' as you call it. I had— I had to make sure that the police wouldn't find out that—that it wasn't me. It—it was a question of—of obliterating his features, John."

There was a nasty silence between them. Stephen Lawlor's hand had begun to shake so violently that he couldn't hold his coffeecup. His face was ravaged by the memory. Again he put up his two hands to hide it.

Kevin could feel the horror; it jumped between them like an electric spark. But he knew, oh, so well, what it was to be hunted.

After a while, the trembling ceased. Lawlor said, in a ghost of his former voice, "Well, it was wrong; it was a crime, I know that. There's no defence. I—I did it. It's done. That's that." He shuddered, and seemed to regain

71

control of himself. "You'll say it was my own fault—a judgment for being—what would you call it? Unmoral." He managed, now, to drink his coffee.

"Anyway, I did it. I got him into my clothes. I rammed my ring on his finger—and my watch—and my wallet."

"And the birthmark."

"Yes, and that. Permanganate of potash and ink. Raôul told me how to do it once—for a short story I was writing. It worked."

"It took me in completely."

Lawlor stared at him. "Yes. I reasoned that if I put your letter in his pocket they'd get hold of you. I reasoned that it—it wouldn't be the sort of job anyone would—linger over."

"Then?"

"I had to think of some way I could fix it so that the—the injuries to the head would seem natural. There wasn't much time, John. I had to do it before rigor set it, and I'd no idea how long that would be. I was nearly mad with indecision. Then— Then I remembered that road. I hadn't been there for ages—not since the last time I went to see Aunt Bella, and I was little more than a kid then.

"Well, I trusted to luck. I got my car round to the lane behind the house—where you climbed the wall—and I managed to heave him across the garden and out to it—through the gate, of course. If the flat had been on any other floor I couldn't have done it. The balcony and staircase saved me.

"I—I drove out to the place. It was there that I made him—unrecognizable. Then I poured petrol over the top half of his body, put him in the driver's seat and let in the clutch."

"You'd have been in the soup if the car hadn't caught fire."

"I know. I was prepared to go down and put a light to it if that happened. But . . . Well, they nearly always do you know. Petrol and a hot engine—it's practically a certainty."

They were both silent again, and then Lawlor said, "You do believe me, don't you, John? I know it sounds mad, but you must believe me."

And this was a turning point.

Up to this moment John Kevin had believed the story implicitly. He too knew what it was like to be hunted; he knew that tingling fear in the small of the back, that pounding of the heart if a car should chance to backfire in the street. But there was something—something he could not quite grasp—which now made him suspicious. Perhaps, when Stephen Lawlor had said, "I know it sounds mad, but you must believe me," his voice had held just a trace too much of pleading, of urgency. It left, in Kevin's mind, a shadow of doubt which had not been there a moment before. But he said, "Yes, of course, I believe you. The odd thing is, somebody's been trying to finish me off, too."

"*You?*"

"Yes, me. Can you explain that?"

Lawlor stared, his eyes huge behind the weird lenses. "No, I cannot. Unless— Unless they think I didn't drop the stuff, after all; unless they think we're some sort of accomplices. After all, we were together in Paris—and now

73

you're in Dublin. And it was you who were called upon to identify me."

This seeemed to ring very true.

"My God, John, if that's the case you'd better get out quick." There was real urgency in his voice now.

And again that obstinate suspicion roused itself in Kevin's brain. He said, "Are you trying to get rid of me, Steve?"

"Hell, no. As far as I'm concerned it's a relief to have you around. But these people are determined; they don't seem to stop at one attempt."

"The point is," Kevin said, "that I can't go. The police have advised me not to—not just yet, anyway."

"Oh, Lord!"

"Exactly. I shall simply have to take care for a few days. What will you do?"

Lawlor frowned. "I'm going to England. I've managed to get hold of a passport; it was pretty tricky, but I've done it."

"How?"

"Oh, my dear John, must you ask how? There are ways and means in every city in the world—providing you can pay. Lachatte does it in Paris; you remember him—you met at the Quatre Arts, that night we did the clubs. Well, it's much the same in Dublin. I have a nose for such things."

"Yes, Steve, you have."

"Why don't you come with me? Tell the guard where you're going. Give them an address. They can hardly hold you."

"I might." Kevin stared dreamily at the smoke-hazed ceiling. "Tell me," he said, "what about Celia?"

"What about her?"

"She's— She seems to have fallen for the fatal charm. Apparently not even the Irish are proof against the Irish."

"She's a child."

Kevin looked at him. "Steve, that girl is suffering; it can do no harm to let her know you're alive. I think she'd hang for you willingly. She certainly wouldn't talk if you asked her not to."

Lawlor smiled slowly. "You incurable, terrifying romantic, John Kevin. Trust a woman! Me? My dear boy!"

"She's suffering, Steve. It's— It's no joke."

"She'll forget. Children have short memories." He noticed the anger in Kevin's eyes and leaned forward. "John, I cannot, I simply *cannot* risk it being known that I wasn't in that car. Be sensible, for heaven's sake. Celia's a sweet creature. I was fond of her, very. But think, John, think of the charges I might have to face if the truth got out. Oh, no, it's asking too much. I can't tell her—and neither must you."

For a long time they stared at each other, their eyes fixed in concentration. Then Kevin glanced away. "All right. I won't say anything—not yet—not without telling you, in any case."

"Not ever, John."

"*Ever*'s a big word. Let's leave it at that. I'm going back to bed, I'm tired."

In the street, where the drizzle slanted across, he said, "When'll you go to England, Steve?"

"Not for a day or two. I'm pretty safe where I live now. And I'd like the hue and cry over my death—" he smiled—"to die down a little. And there's no harm in keeping an eye on you, John. Romantics are dangerous."

75

"I won't let you down, Steve. But I do think it's only common decency to let Celia know. Supposing she sees you in the street, or Uncle Edward Dillon—he's met you, he says—or even Finian."

"People don't look for a dead man in the street," replied Lawlor with truth. "Besides, generally speaking, I don't go out much, and if I do I muffle myself up, as now."

Certainly, Kevin thought, glancing at him, he was quite unrecognizable to the casual glance, hunched into his overcoat collar, shabby hat pulled down, spectacles glinting. No, this was not the Stephen Lawlor the world knew. In spite of himself Kevin had to admire the man.

Lawlor said, "We'll go our own ways at this corner. It's a foul night." Then, after a pause, "By the way, John, you did say that you hadn't taken anything from the flat, didn't you?"

"Yes." He could feel the diary, suddenly heavy against his leg. "Why? Have you missed something? The police were there, you know."

"Nothing important." And his eyes, as they parted, were very bright, very piercing. He said again, "No, nothing important."

"Can I get in touch with you?"

Lawlor produced a card from his pocket.

"You can ring this number and leave a message for Mr. Byrne; it's a small newspaper shop. I'll ring you back."

"That's not very trusting," said Kevin, pocketing the card.

"Romantics," Stephen Lawlor replied, "are not particularly trustworthy people." And he turned and walked away into the drizzling darkness.

## II

John Kevin let himself into Uncle Edward Dillon's house with the latchkey which Finian had procured for him. He had not reached the foot of the staircase, however, before the library door opened, and Celia, in her dressing gown, confronted him.

"I heard you go out," she said. "You really shouldn't—not without Finian."

He followed her into the library, and she closed the door.

"The two of you came in," she continued, "and then, about half an hour later, you went out alone. What've you been up to?"

"Sleuthing."

"Have you discovered anything?"

He glanced at her sharply then. She sat, swinging a loose slipper from her toe, on the arm of her uncle's Chippendale chair. In her camel's hair, schoolgirl's dressing gown she looked about sixteen years old.

Prevaricating, he said, "Excuse my asking, but how old *are* you?"

"I'm twenty-one this autumn."

He was astonished; she surveyed his astonishment calmly. "You see," she said, "I'm not so much of a child, after all. When I said I loved Steve, I meant it."

Again, as he had seen it before, a sudden spasm of pain crossed her face, making her for a moment quite haggard. She repeated it: "Have you discovered anything?"

Kevin said, "No." And at that moment he realized that he disliked Stephen Lawlor very much indeed. It is almost impossible for an honest person to tell lies for someone else without disliking him. Love, of course, is the exception; it always is.

He said it again: "No, nothing," and could willingly have wrung Lawlor's neck.

The girl stood up and trailed wearily away to the window. "I can't sleep," she said. "Last night I couldn't sleep, either. I didn't *know* anything then, but I was afraid for him. I think perhaps you really can feel things like that about someone you love—a sort of sixth sense. As soon as that telephone call came, during dinner, I was afraid. Don't ask me why; I just was."

Kevin was startled. He could hardly bear to look at her misery, but what she had said outweighed his pity.

"During dinner?" he echoed.

"Yes. I told you, didn't I? We had dinner together at the Bailey last night—only a few hours before it happened. That's how I was so sure he wasn't drunk."

"And there was a telephone call?"

"Yes."

"And then?"

"Then he became . . . Oh, I tried to explain this afternoon. Sort of excited—nervous. He said he had to go some-

78

where; he made some silly excuse, I forgot just what. He was lying, anyway."

"Oh, damn it," shouted Kevin, suddenly giving vent to his fury. "You know that he lied to you, and yet you loved him!"

She turned and stared very gravely, not looking like a child any more. "Have you never been in love?" she asked gently. "What does a lie matter one way or the other?"

He felt a fool then.

"Try, try, try," she said, "to think of me as grown-up. I am, you know."

It didn't fit, of course. It didn't make sense—Stephen Lawlor being called away from dinner with an attractive girl, to find with surprise that there was a dead man in his flat. There could be explanations—there could always be explanations—but in this case the *atmosphere* was wrong. Hadn't Celia herself said that, over tea at the hotel? "The atmosphere was all wrong," she had said. "It didn't add up."

Nothing added up, and that was a fact.

He began to stride about the big room, fiercely uneasy, while she watched him from the window. He must *think;* he must get all this phantasmagoria of fact and fiction into some sort of order in his mind. The overwhelming certainty that Lawlor's story was half true and half a lie rose up and seized him, he couldn't escape it. "I know it sounds mad, but you must believe me," he had said—and there had been too much urgency in his voice. Yet that story had been so eminently true in feeling: improbable, yes, but then Stephen Lawlor's life had that quality.

Celia said, "John, I want to ask you something."

He stopped his pacing and stared at her.

"I want to ask you a favour."

"Ask away."

Dark eyes very direct, wearing that courage which he had found so moving before, she said, "Please, will you go back to England, and give up this—this thing?"

Before he could draw breath to answer she left the window and came near to him. "No, don't be angry. Listen to me first. I don't want you to—to find out about Steve."

"My dear girl . . ."

"I've no excuses; it sounds crazy, I know." She faced him, holding both his arms, trying to snare him with those eyes. "Leave well alone," she said.

"Leave *well* alone!" For an instant he thought that perhaps she actually knew that Lawlor was alive. Then, again, he saw the anguish which she could not properly hide. "Leave *well* alone!" he repeated.

"All right." She continued to stare. "Leave bad alone, if you must have it that way. Please."

Avoiding her eyes, he said, "You're afraid, you mean, of what the truth may be?"

"Yes, I am. Perhaps it's silly, but I want Steve's memory left clean, even if—even if his life wasn't always that way."

Wonderingly he said, "You really loved him, didn't you?"

"Yes." Seeing that he wouldn't look at her, she released his arms. "Steve asked me to marry him."

Kevin nodded. Dear God, he thought, how many times had he heard that one? Barbara, in Portsmouth during the war, and a girl called Anna in Naples, and some young

80

American in London, with red hair—he'd forgotten her name—and even Lucille, in Paris, who should have known better. And others, too.

He beat his fists together in impotent rage. What in the name of the devil did women see in Steve Lawlor? It was a mystery.

Glancing at this girl, so still, so anguished, so inexperienced, standing before him in her schoolgirl's dressing gown, he knew that he could not speak to her. Mere words meant nothing in the face of magic. But if he could not counter the Lawlor spell, he was certainly not going to become ensnared by it himself. So, quite firmly, he said, "No. I'm damned if I'll go back to England."

She assimilated this. Then: "I won't help you any more."

"I don't expect you to."

She became undecided suddenly. "Oh, dear," she said, "you'll get hurt. You aren't practical enough."

"No." He looked at her directly now. "I'm not the one who'll get hurt." He had seen, very clearly, the monstrous thing that Stephen Lawlor was doing to this girl; not even he, hating Lawlor as he did at that moment, could have brought himself to tell her the vicious truth: that all her suffering, her sleeplessness and her splendid loyalty were a ridiculous joke because the man whose memory she defended was alive and laughing at her.

The pity and the beastliness of it caught at John Kevin's throat; he could no longer bear to be in the same room with her.

"I'm—I'm sorry I can't do as you ask," he said. "Good night." And he practically ran from the room.

The first thing he did, when he had shut the bedroom door behind him, was to examine Stephen Lawlor's diary. He had been wanting to do this ever since it had come into his possession, but the opportunity had hardly presented itself. He could not banish from his mind the too casual way in which Lawlor had asked whether he had removed anything from the flat. Therefore, Kevin reasoned, there must have been something in it which he did not wish to fall into the hands of a stranger.

Full of excitement he sat down on his bed and opened the diary; full of mounting excitement he scrutinized each page. Gradually the excitement gave way to uncertainty, to perplexity, to baffled irritation.

It was evident from the start that Lawlor used it as an appointment book; the entries consisted mostly of names with a time and a place. Thus Kevin saw, "Lucille, 9:30, Jean-Pierre's," or "Jack and Polly, 1:00, Maxim's," and even "John K . . ." (himself) ". . . Hotel Siena, 7:15."

What was more maddening still, was the fact that the entries ended altogether on the day Lawlor had arrived in Dublin. Not even his appointments with Celia were listed —and the remaining pages were blank, until the three at the end set aside for memoranda. These, as in all diaries, were a jumble of notes for shopping, odd telephone numbers—all Parisian in this case—and jotted train, or possibly aeroplane, timetables. One entry only struck Kevin as meaningless, and therefore interesting: it simply ran, "D.J. 121." And on second thoughts, it was probably a car number plate. Kevin swore, and went to bed.

But if he had supposed that his utter weariness portended a night's deep sleep he was wrong. In the first place, he lay awake for over an hour with no sign of drowsiness whatever. And, later, if he did sleep, there was no division between his dreams and his waking thoughts. A jumble of faces and voices and disembodied questions seethed through the byways of his brain. And always, at the centre, like some nightmare by a surrealist sculptor stood the figure of Stephen Lawlor—a surrealist figure of incomplete entities, revolving slowly to show new, incomplete facets: a figure without arms, or with arms where the legs should have been; a figure with no head—or with a battered head, bleeding and ghastly; a figure that smiled or menaced; eyes behind monstrous, distorting lenses, which glared, dissolved, were sightless.

Celia said, "Steve was a fine man."

The old vulture in Merrion Square flapped his arms and cried, "A seeker after Truth. A crusader, sir, with a flaming sword of Truth in his hand."

Celia said, "He was so warm, generous, exciting to be with."

Old Uncle Edward Dillon said, "Everything connected with that family is apt to be fantastic."

Finian said, "Mr. Lawlor was a fine, swaggering buckaroo to turn any girl's heart."

Celia said, "I loved him. . . . He asked me to marry him."

And, staring so intently, so innocently behind those weird spectacles, Lawlor said in that soft, charming voice, "You know, John, I don't really think I'm a dishonest person, do you?"

Dear God!

Kevin flung back the bedclothes and leapt out of bed.

He stood, wild and dishevelled in the middle of the room, hands clenching and unclenching.

Honesty! Dishonesty! And, across the passageway, lay the girl who would not allow Stephen Lawlor's memory to be stained. Dear God!

After a time he grew calmer. He stood at the window staring out, watching the dawn flower into a cold, grey sky. And he faced the facts.

Fact Number One: He did not believe the story which Lawlor had told him. It was a clever story, told by a consummate artist—by a liar, that is to say, who was so carried along on the wave crest of his own lies that to him they became real.

Fact Number Two: If he did not believe this story, then he must find another, a true one, to refute it.

Fact Number Three: Until he had done this he must not run squealing to the police.

Fact Number Four: He must not tell Celia that Lawlor was alive, but he must make certain that in the end, somehow, she knew the truth. Better this cruel truth than a more cruel falsehood.

Fact Number Five: He had omitted to follow many valuable clues. He must find (1) the old vulture; (2) the man whose photograph he had taken in the hotel foyer; (3) the caretaker of the flat, who must know something of value, however small; (4) the waiter or commissionaire at the Bailey who had taken the telephone call summoning Lawlor from dinner on the night in question; and (5) . . .

Yes. Number Five was the keystone of the arch, the stone which he must remove to bring all Stephen Lawlor's lies tumbling about his head. Find Number Five: Who exactly was the man who had died, how did he die—and why?

Strangely enough, he did not care now that he had slept so little and so restlessly. His head was suddenly clear and he was filled with a furious, impatient energy. The things that had happened in the last two days—some mad, some meaningless, some fraught with hidden meanings, some terrifying—all crystallized at this dawn-lit moment into a strong, indomitable purpose.

John Kevin was set for battle, and the enemy was not necessarily Stephen Lawlor; the enemy was evil, lies, dishonesty, brutality . . . The old enemy, as old as the human soul. Stephen Lawlor was safe so long as he did not incorporate those enemies in his being. If he did—and Kevin was going to find out—then God help him.

# III

Celia, lying awake on the other side of the corridor, must have heard him moving about. Once again she intercepted him; once again in her childish dressing gown she called to him, but this time from the top of the stairs.

"John?"

He turned, already halfway down, and looked back at her.

"Where are you going?"

He did not reply, but stared at her—a long, direct stare—and the quality of it disturbed her; there was an authority and a defiance in it which she did not associate with John Kevin. Then he turned, ran down the last flight, across the hall and out of the house.

He went to the nearest café which was open at that early hour and ordered a large breakfast. During it he read all the available newspapers; there was no mention of the sudden disappearance of a man in Dublin. He had hardly expected that there would be—yet.

When he had finished eating he went straight to the

flats and in at the front entrance. A middle-aged man, broad in the beam, was polishing the hall in a desultory fashion, whistling, "I know that my Redeemer liveth," through his teeth. No one else stirred in the place; it was only half-past seven.

Kevin, in his new mood of furious impatience, did not mince matters in any way. He held out a ten-shilling note and said, "I want to know anything you can tell me about Mr. Lawlor, who was using Mr. Grant's flat. If anything you say is of value I'll give you another of these afterwards."

The man goggled and looked at the note curiously, as if expecting it to be poisoned. Then, cautiously, he took it and held it between finger and thumb. Presently his mouth twisted into a smile, and the smile bloomed into a grin so wide that it reminded Kevin inevitably of the Cheshire Cat.

"D'you know what?" the man said finally, still grinning. "You're an act of God, that's what you are. For there was I, as gloomy as Monday morning because I hadn't a shilling to put on Esterella at Clonmel—that mare's going to win, take my word for it—and here you come like the Angel Gabriel himself with gold in your hand. Lord have mercy on us." And, to Kevin's relief, he asked no questions as to the why and wherefore of this enquiry, but settled himself in a comfortable leaning position on his mop and devoted himself absolutely to the subject in question. "Now," he said, "and what is it you're after knowing about poor Mr. Lawlor, God rest his soul?"

"I want to know whether he had any visitors—that you saw or spoke to."

87

"He did," replied the caretaker with spirit, "and I'll tell you how I know so certain: because the guard asked just that question only yesterday—a nasty, nosy, stuck-up little popinjay of a man calling himself a chief inspector . . ."

Kevin grinned at this description of O'Connor.

". . . and I said divil a word. Because why? I'll tell you. Because it's them with their nasty, prying ways that makes half the trouble in the world."

"Mr. Lawlor's visitors," Kevin reminded him.

"Aren't I telling you? I lay in bed last night and I thought of what I might have told the guard, if they hadn't been so stuck-up and full of theirselves. He had five that I know of—besides Miss Celia Dillon, Mr. Tony Grant's cousin. I'm not counting her."

"Men or women?"

"One woman—and she no better than she should have been, if you ask me."

"We'll forget her then. How about the men?"

The caretaker picked his teeth reflectively. "I'll tell you something," he said, after a small pause. "They were for-eigners."

Kevin was startled. "How d'you mean, foreigners?"

"Aren't I telling you?" He ruminated again. "I only spoke to two of them, mind you, but they weren't Irish-men, no, not a one of them."

"English perhaps," said Kevin, grinning.

"Maybe, maybe. But not educated fellows like yourself. One was all *r*'s and blather—I hardly understood a word. He wanted a taxi, and, bless my soul, how the poor man did create. 'Who d'you think I am?' I said. 'D'you think I have magic at me fingertips,' I said, 'to go making taxis out of thin air in a back street in Dublin on a Saturday night?' "

"And the other?"

"I understood divil a word of him either: all *ah*'s and *er*'s and grunting like an old pig stuck fast in a bog. He wanted to know the way to his hotel, and like a child he was, not understanding a word I said. He came twice, this feller."

"You can remember when?"

"Sure, I can, for it was me day off on Wednesday last week, and he came in on the Tuesday and Thursday. I tell you, I thought it all up for the guard, and if they hadn't been so cocky and conceited I'd have told them. Mind you, I might not have noticed these fellers at all—except that they all looked alike. If they hadn't been different I'd have said they were all the same chap, I would."

Kevin laughed at this Irishism. He could not quite place these men, but the oddity of them was not lost on him. He said, "How were they dressed?"

"Oh, tidily enough. But nivver a one of them was a gentleman, that I'll swear. Heavy men, if you follow me. Clumsy sort of fellers."

"I see. And this hotel one of them wanted to get to, d'you recall the name of it?"

"I do. For it's a terrible, dirty hole, and I didn't like to think of a visitor staying there at all."

"What was it?"

"The Alpha in Westland Row, not far from the station." The caretaker sniffed.

"Now," said Kevin, "the night before last—that's the night Mr. Lawlor had his accident—do you remember if

89

there was a visitor then, say, between eight and nine o'clock?"

But it was too much to hope that the man could answer this vital question with accuracy. And there was always the back way in—through the garden and via the balcony. Anybody *could* have entered the flat without being seen.

However, Kevin was pleased with what he had discovered. He was beginning to realize that in this matter it was the least sensible details which seemed most pregnant with possibility. Stephen Lawlor's four visitors, for instance—the "heavy men," the "clumsy sort of fellers"—were significant because, in some way, they did not fit. They were menacing in their new, but characteristic clothes. They were part of a pattern which he could not yet discern.

Yes, he was pleased. He handed over a second note, said that he hoped Esterella might do all that was expected of her at Clonmel, and left the caretaker leaning on his mop. That broad grin, like the grin of the Cheshire Cat, seemed to linger long after the man himself was out of view.

Kevin went straight to Westland Row, near the station, and found the Alpha Hotel without difficulty. It was exactly what he had expected: a small Georgian house, painted pale green, with a blatant chromium name plate over the graceful door. Inside, the paint was less fresh and the décor Victorian; there was the usual smell of stale cabbage.

Even now it was only eight o'clock, and apart from a worried Eurasian who had a train to catch there was no one about.

It saddened Kevin to think of all the Alpha Hotels in

all the streets near railway stations, and of all the worried Eurasians who had trains to catch and could find no one to give them their bill.

Eventually, however, a greasy slut appeared, handed the dark gentleman a slip of paper in exchange for his money, sniffed, and looked wearily at Kevin.

"No rooms," she said. "Full up till the end of next week. Sorry."

Kevin hastily assured her that he didn't want a room. "I was wondering," he said, "if a friend of mine stayed here last week—a Mr. O'Neill?"

As he hoped she opened a visitors' book which lay on a bamboo table in a recess under the stairs. Looking over her shoulder while she hunted for the mystical Mr. O'Neill (and wondering how it was possible to wash so little and keep one's self-respect) he saw that only three men had stayed for any length of time during the week in question. The Alpha Hotels of the world cater mostly to one-night visitors—and, often, for double rooms at odd hours. Of these three, one had brought his wife and daughter also, and, although this did not entirely exclude him, it seemed unlikely that Lawlor's visitors—if, indeed, they were up to no good—would travel with their families.

The remaining two names were a Mr. James O'Leary of Belfast and a Mr. B. Tanner of Newcastle-on-Tyne, England.

Kevin knew that he had been lucky again. Once again something fell into place with satisfying clarity: Mr. B. Tanner of Newcastle-on-Tyne might well find it difficult to understand the caretaker, and vice versa. There was something of typical Irish vividness about that description

91

of Mr. B. Tanner, too: "All *ah*'s and *er*'s and grunting like an old pig stuck fast in a bog." Yes, it was right; it fitted. Doubtless no professional detective would have accepted it as a clue, but to Kevin, lifted on this new impatience and carried along on a wave of excitement, it was good enough for the time being. A picture was forming in his naturally pictorial mind. Stephen Lawlor had wanted a flat in Dublin, a private place in which to meet these four men, these "clumsy sort of fellers." Why?

He gave the slut half a crown, to her surprise, and hurried out of the fusty, cabbage-smelling gloom into brilliant, early-morning sunshine.

Since the two clues which he had taken the trouble to pursue had proved so rewarding, he began to search his brain for others: small details, perhaps, which he had overlooked or thought insignificant.

It was too early yet to make enquiries at the Bailey—where Lawlor had taken Celia to dinner on the vital evening. Kevin therefore went to St. Stephens Green and sat there on a seat, in sunshine and solitude, watching the ducks perform their morning toilet by the edge of the lake.

More and more he began to see the paradox of detection —that the important pieces to the puzzle were the ones that didn't fit, that didn't make sense. Stephen Lawlor was an excellent driver; therefore it hadn't made sense that he should have an accident, sober, on a comparatively easy corner. He had come to Ireland to visit an aunt some thirty miles from Dublin—an aunt, moreover, who intended to leave him her house and money; therefore it didn't make sense that he should have to take a flat in Dublin, and that he should not go near the aunt in ten whole days. And so on.

Casting his mind to and fro in the dark cave of senseless happenings, Kevin remembered the old vulture in Merrion Square. Now *there* was senselessness in perfection. The crazy, uncontrolled voice rang in his memory: "A great and terrible man. A fighter, Mr. Kevin. A seeker after Truth. A crusader for Freedom, sir, with a flaming sword of Truth in his hand." Yes, indeed, as applied to Stephen Lawlor, here was the acme of senselessness—and yet with it, as with much madness, a kind of wild reason. There was in Lawlor something of the fire which must have driven a Crusader forth to the Holy Land; often Kevin had heard it said that if only the man's restless energy, his unpredictable enthusiasm, could be harnessed, what good might he not do for mankind. And it was true. For it was Stephen Lawlor, regardless of himself, who had leapt overboard after the young seaman on that stormy day in mid-Channel; it was Stephen Lawlor to whom the nuns of Dijon had receipted a gift of fifty pounds—extorted, no doubt, from some rich and exasperated casual acquaintance after hours of rhetoric. "A crusader for Freedom, sir, with a sword of . . ."

Freedom!

Kevin sat up straight on his park bench. What about that pamphlet then? The United Freedom Movement? A pamphlet printed in London, certainly, but might there not be a branch in Dublin? And might not the old vulture, with his mad eyes, have belonged to just such an organization? Might that not be his point of contact with Stephen Lawlor?

He jumped to his feet, alarming the ducks somewhat, and

hurried towards the gates of the gardens, to where, he knew, there stood a public telephone box.

Luck was certainly on his side this morning, for not only was there a directory in the box, but the pages he required had actually not been torn out. And luck persisted: there was, at 144 Antrim Street, a branch of the United Freedom Movement.

Round the corner of the square, opposite the Melbourne, he recalled that he had seen a taxi rank. It proved only a short ride to the corner of Antrim Street and Rose Road. He told the driver to wait and went to look at number 144. The houses here were Victorian and hideous with capacious areas and basements. The United Freedom Movement, he was not surprised to discover, inhabited the basement. A glass-fronted case was wired to the railings, and inside it various inaccurately typed notices proclaimed the Movement's activities. These, somewhat surprisingly, were various and many. That very evening, for instance, Mr. Thomas Muspratt was due to speak on "Freedom and the Controlled Society," whatever that might be. Kevin noticed that "all friends, whether members or not," were welcome. Mr. Muspratt would begin at seven o'clock, after which there would be an informal discussion and refreshments. It sounded, Kevin thought, horrific, but he intended to put in an appearance.

He returned to the taxi and asked the driver to take him back to Grafton Street. It was now past nine o'clock, and the shops had opened for the day. He went to one of the big chemists and gave them the roll of film, in which, he hoped, would be a clear enough picture of the man who had watched and waited for him in the foyer of the Melbourne. He asked for an express printing of number five on the reel and was pleased to hear that he could have it any time after three in the afternoon.

He considered that since on a normal day he would not yet be out of bed, he had done a good morning's work. He bought the later papers—as many English ones as possible included—and retired for a coffee.

The papers were depressing. In each of them a case was reported concerning a woman who had been murdered by a "gentleman friend," and whose disappearance had not been reported for a whole month. "We thought," her mother was quoted as saying, "that our Queenie had gone to stay with her fiancé in Manchester." Yes, it was depressing; it might, he saw clearly now, be a good month before he was given any clue as to the identity of the man who had died for Stephen Lawlor and even then the report of it might not be made public.

No, there must be some other clue—some tiny, insignificant pointer to show him the way to this knowledge. For he must, he *must* discover who the man was. The more he considered it the more certain he became that the identity of the dead body was the key to the whole labyrinthine business.

He was still considering this when he emerged from the coffee shop and walked slowly down Grafton Street towards the Bailey.

The brilliant day had died young, and the sky was in mourning for it. Presently, without doubt, it would rain. And his luck seemed to have changed with the weather, for no one at the restaurant could remember taking a telephone call for a Mr. Lawlor on Monday evening at about eight o'clock.

It was a chastened John Kevin who stood undecided on the pavement of Duke Street biting his lower lip, lost in a sea of surmise.

Finally he turned and strolled back into Grafton Street again. He felt tired suddenly; his sleepless night had overtaken him and he could hardly keep his eyes open.

Damn the whole business, he thought. There were too many facets to it—too many unanswerable questions; and he remembered suddenly the Tara Lounge—the final, unutterable enigma. He was extremely depressed.

Then he saw the wedding group.

He would never know the name of the happily united couple whose entirely vacant, and really very unattractive, faces caught his eye and thus changed the whole course of his life. They stood, grinning oafishly, amid a phalanx of relations, with two villainous infants in satin at their feet. It was the kind of photograph which gave John Kevin, photographer, savage delight. He stood staring in wonder, drinking his fill. And, as he turned away, he noticed a board upon which was fixed an assortment of astonishing faces; and across the top of the board was a notice saying, *Passport Photographs, 3/6d.*

Suddenly John Kevin was aware of a glimmer of light. It bloomed, it flowered, it glared.

Passports! Yes, passports. Whatever Stephen Lawlor might say—sipping his coffee and peering over those strange lenses—it was *not* easy to procure an illegal passport in a strange city, not at short notice in any case, and certainly not one you could trust, one you could be sure

96

hadn't been stolen and was not therefore on the police list.

And yet Stephen Lawlor was possessed of a passport, an English one. How?

The probable answer was clear, and electrifying. He had taken it out of the dead man's pocket; he had exchanged identities with the dead man.

If this was so, and if Kevin could look at that passport, *he would know the dead man's name.*

## IV

Now HE WAS really excited—for this might well be the turning point of the whole matter. Men were not killed for no reason—there was always a motive—and once, Kevin argued, he could disclose the motive in this case, he would be well on the way to making sense of what lay behind it.

He was preoccupied with these thoughts when he let himself into Uncle Edward Dillon's house and came face to face with a young policeman.

"Oh," said Kevin.

The guard nodded towards the library. "Inspector O'Connor's in there, sir."

He had no sooner spoken than the door opened, and O'Connor, like a cuckoo in a clock, shot out. "You'll come in here, Mr. Kevin, please," he snapped.

Kevin, feeling like a small boy summoned to the headmaster's study, obeyed.

He found Celia, Edward Dillon and Finian, looking either truculent or sheepish, or both.

"Now," said the Inspector briskly, "since the *family* is assembled—" He glared at John Kevin.

"You will be good enough," said Uncle Edward calmly, "to use your manners in my house, Inspector. I'm a taxpayer, and I don't take insolence from public servants. Mr. Kevin here is my guest. What's so strange in that?"

"He said," snapped O'Connor, "that he didn't know Miss Dillon's address."

"At that time," replied Kevin, "I didn't. In any case, you may remember I added that even if I did I wouldn't tell you."

"Ah." Uncle Edward cut in neatly before the Inspector could reply. "You see, sir, it's as I said. A little more tact on your part would elicit a lot more information."

O'Connor laughed unpleasantly; he was obviously very angry. "Very well," he said, "you all insist on taking this attitude—that's your own affair. In legal circles it's known as obstruction."

"In my case," interposed Uncle Edward, "it is *objection*—to the manner in which you conduct your business. However, you were saying—?"

"You all insist," went on O'Connor, ignoring him, "that you know nothing of what brought the late Mr. Lawlor to Dublin."

"His aunt," Celia began, "was . . ."

"His *real* reason for coming." The Inspector was clearly going to brook no further insubordination. "There is no doubt whatever that Mr. Lawlor did not meet his death by accident; there is no reason to suppose that it was a case of suicide. The alternative, therefore, is that he was killed deliberately by a person or persons unknown. I should have thought that you, as his friends, would wish such a matter to be cleared up. . . ."

There was silence. Celia, Edward Dillon, Kevin and Finian stared blankly.

O'Connor swore under his breath. "You persist in this obstruction . . ."

Yes, for their own reasons, they persisted: Kevin, because he knew that Lawlor was not dead; Celia, because of her loyalty to someone she had loved; Uncle Edward, because he disliked O'Connor's truculent manner; and Finian, because he was a trusty retainer, and mortal enemy of the police, in any case.

"All right," snapped the Inspector. "But I need hardly add that your attitude will figure in my report."

Still silence.

"And I suppose I am to presume that no one in this room knows that a forced entry was made into the premises previously inhabited by Mr. Lawlor?"

Silence of the grave.

O'Connor examined each face in turn. Then he gave one of his infuriating nods. "The truth," he said, "will be made clear in the end—you need not doubt that. And your part of it may well cause you all grave inconvenience."

"Our consciences," replied Uncle Edward placidly, "are at peace."

The Inspector snorted, spun around, and marched out of the room. His exit was followed by another silence. Then Uncle Edward glanced at Finian. "Go and see them off the premises, there's a good fellow." Finian grinned in a manner only to be described as wolfish, and obeyed with alacrity.

100

"Our consciences," said Uncle Edward again, when the door had closed, "are at peace." He glanced from one to the other of the young people gravely, but nearly smiling.

Celia looked out of the window and Kevin stared at the ceiling.

"I think," added the old gentleman, "that it's as well *I* spoke those words." He chuckled, and then, since the girl and the young man both turned on him, "No. I do *not* wish to be enlightened. If you choose to cock snooks at authority that—as the truculent Inspector would say—is your affair. Personally I find it very proper in the young." He chuckled again, looking, Kevin thought, more than ever like the Devil in mellow mood and disguise. "I," the Devil concluded, "am no longer young. I have my immortal soul to consider."

And, still chuckling, he left the room.

Celia leaned on the windowsill and regarded John Kevin thoughtfully. "Why didn't *you* tell the Inspector what you know?" she enquired finally.

"Because you've asked me to keep quiet."

"And yet you won't do the other thing I ask?"

He frowned.

"You won't pack your bag and catch the next plane out of Dublin."

It pained him that he should mean so very little to her. It was almost as if Stephen Lawlor possessed her soul like an evil spirit; nothing else mattered. After the momentary pain came anger.

"No, I will not leave Dublin," he said. "I've considered your feelings, yes, because you've been kind to me and because I like and respect you. But I'm damned if I'll run

101

away just because you happen to be obsessed by the idea of Steve Lawlor—and, consequently, to have formed an entirely mistaken opinion of him."

"I've admitted that I'm probably mistaken," she said, and her honesty—and a kind of dignity that went with it—was touching.

Oddly enough, though touched, he grew more angry; the resentment he felt against Lawlor welled up inside him.

"I thought," said Celia, "that I'd made it quite clear that I loved him. You can't cut off love like—like an electric light."

"I'm not talking about love," replied Kevin furiously. "I'm talking about truth. I'm going to find out the truth about Steve Lawlor if it takes me ten years."

"Why?" She faced him now, eyes blazing and faint colour touching her cheekbones.

"Someone tried to kill me. Isn't that good enough reason? Dear God, are you so besotted with this man that you can't see the difference between good and evil?"

"I don't *care*." Her fists were clenched now. "He may have done things he shouldn't have done. Who hasn't? But he's dead, and it's all over. Leave him alone, can't you?"

It was on the tip of Kevin's tongue, then, to tell her the truth, but he held himself in check; he shut his mouth tight, and bent every nerve at his command in an effort to control the temper that pounded inside him. For a long time—or so it seemed—he stood, tense and strained, confronting her. And he won his battle.

But she had seen the change in him, and it frightened her. She had seen how that inner conflict ravaged his face

102

—how the pulse throbbed at his temple, and how his anger had abated, leaving him cold and exhausted. This intense self-control alarmed her more than the fury.

And when he said, "Forgive me. I—I'm sorry," something turned over in her heart. She sensed suddenly that she, in her imagination, had touched only the edge of Stephen's secret business. For the first time it struck her that there might indeed have been depths to him at which she could not guess—dared not guess.

She longed to ask the fair, stricken young man before her what he guessed the unhappy truth to be, the truth which he was so determined to discover. And yet she could not bring herself to destroy—or to risk destroying— her memory of the man she had loved.

For the first time it entered her head that perhaps she was running away from the truth in order to preserve a precious memory, and, because she was honest at all times, the thought was unpleasant to her. It smacked of hypocrisy, which she loathed. A terrible certainty assailed her that her love could not live with the truth which John Kevin suspected, and meant to reveal.

So, in a conflict of emotions, she turned and ran out of the room, tears pressing at the corners of her eyes. But, as soon as she had shut the door behind her, she was seized by a sense of her own cowardice. She stood for a moment, hands pressed to her cheeks, eyes half-closed, caught in an agony of indecision.

Perhaps she stayed thus for a few seconds, perhaps for a few minutes; time has little meaning in moments of strong emotional stress. However long it may have been, she turned finally, meaning to go back and ask Kevin plainly what it was that he knew or suspected.

But as she put her hand on the doorknob she heard his voice speaking on the telephone, and indecision returned.

Kevin had taken from his pocket the piece of card on which Stephen Lawlor had written the telephone number which might be used for getting in touch with "Mr. Byrne." In this case, however, he was not going to give Lawlor a chance to ring him back. He had other plans.

He said, "I believe I can leave a message with you for a friend of mine called Byrne."

"You can," replied a woman's voice.

"Will you ask him to meet me at the Mooneys' house on the corner of Abbey Street in half an hour's time? That's at midday. Will you say that it's very urgent, and will you tell him on no account to ring me back, because it might cause trouble."

". . . 'because it might,' " intoned the voice, " 'cause trouble.' Yes, I'll tell him that."

"You think he'll be available?"

"Sure, he'll be available. If he's going out he lets me know."

Kevin replaced the receiver. He had an idea that Stephen Lawlor might be a man with a guilty conscience—if, indeed, he had a conscience at all—and that it would be this, as much as anything else, which would bring him hurrying to the rendezvous at the Mooneys'.

It was a long, gloomy bar divided into partitions by wooden screens. In the darkest of the partitions, leaning against the screen with his back to the door, Kevin found Stephen Lawlor. The two men looked at each other in a strange silence, as if, for the first time, they were aware of antagonism between them. It was a brave stare, since neither could afford to antagonize the other at this juncture. Indeed, it struck Kevin suddenly that they stood, the two of them, on the thinnest of thin ice—he with suspicion, and this man in the fantastic spectacles with a load of unguessable secrets, some of them assuredly guilty. The compulsion which kept Stephen Lawlor in Dublin must, Kevin thought suddenly, be as strong as that which kept himself from betraying Stephen Lawlor to the police. It was an entirely dreamlike situation, yet it clearly existed; and this tingling of antagonism was a product of it. They were, he realized, antagonists; and they were joining in single combat as surely as any two ancients, armour-clad and visored.

They stared at each other.

"Well," said Lawlor, "what's your so important news?"

Kevin, sensing now the other's impatience, let it grow stronger while he ordered two glasses of dry sherry as slowly as he could.

When the barman had delivered the drinks and been paid for them, Lawlor said again, "Come on. Let's have it—if, in fact, there *is* any news."

"A chap's been hanging around asking for you," lied Kevin easily. He was pleased to notice an imperceptible tightening of the facial muscles.

"Oh?" said Lawlor. It was impossible not to admire his self-control.

"Yes." Kevin was aware of his own pounding heart;

he saw in his mind's eye the rather childish signature in the visitor's book at the Alpha Hotel. "A Mr. Tanner," he said. "Big chap. Sounded like a Geordie."

He had hoped, admittedly, that this shaft would go home, but he was not prepared for the exactness of his aim. Stephen Lawlor's eyes widened, the blood drained from his face, and he slammed his glass down on the marble bar so hard that a chip flew off the base of it and tinkled onto the floor.

There was a long silence.

"Of course," said Kevin, "I couldn't tell him where you were because I didn't know; and anyway I couldn't be sure that he really was a friend."

"Hardly a friend," said Lawlor in an astonishingly controlled voice. "Rather embarrassing, though, in the circumstances."

"Well—" Kevin prepared shaft number two. "I rather got the impression that he knew you weren't dead." He thought he detected another hit, but the man was controlled now. It was hard to tell, particularly with the eyes so effectively hidden.

It struck him, now, that he might also have made a grave mistake. If this Mr. Tanner was in any way an accomplice, then he would probably know where to get in touch with Stephen Lawlor. Yes, he had gone too far. The only thing he had conclusively proved was that he was onto the right track; there could be no doubting the extent of that first shock at the mention of Mr. Tanner's name.

Quickly, to cover up what he felt to be a mistake, he fired shaft number three and last. "By the way, Steve, we've had the police around. They don't think it was an accident, they think you were murdered. They're getting pretty nosy."

Lawlor smiled gently, and something in the quality of that smile made Kevin feel sure of himself. "I thought you'd like to know," he added.

"Thanks, John." Lawlor was grave now—thoughtful. "I don't think I shall be in Dublin much longer." He finished his sherry.

There was something in this reflective, interested stare which John Kevin found most uncomfortable. He had hoped, too, that Lawlor would talk a little more, would possibly reveal more of himself by so doing. This thoughtful silence was therefore doubly unnerving. Quite clearly Stephen Lawlor was not talking. He merely said again, "Thanks, John." He turned up his coat collar. "You're a man," he added, "of many parts, aren't you?" And he contrived, somehow, to make this a threat—a threat so deadly, because so casual, that John Kevin felt again the prickle of physical fear up his spine.

He knew at that instant—and he wondered how in heaven it had not been obvious before—that this quiet, controlled man facing him, a man whom he had thought to be his friend, was already responsible for those two attempts on his life. The thought was so simple and so logical that it left him witless, rooted to the floor of the bar.

But why? And why, if that was the case, had Lawlor revealed his identity, and the fact that he was still alive? There had been no need to do so. John Kevin, staring amazed at those owlish panes of glass which served Stephen Lawlor as a mask, could see very clearly the shape of events, but the *reason* for them escaped him utterly. The reason, so simple, so childishly plain, was hidden just as the eyes were hidden.

"Yes," said Lawlor gently, "a busy little man of many parts." And he turned and walked away down the length of the bar.

John Kevin was so dumbfounded by this new facet of the business in hand that he nearly forgot why he had asked the man to meet him. He was absolutely certain now that Lawlor had been the driving force behind the blow which had sent him spinning under the wheels of a lorry, that it had been Lawlor's wish that the electric light should be harnessed to the door handle in the hotel bedroom. Yet it was difficult to assimilate, difficult to believe that his old friend, with whom he had laughed and caroused and gone wenching, should wish him dead. Only when he thought, suddenly, of Celia—of her loyalty and love turned into a mockery—did he see that his own situation was part and parcel of the same callous indifference. He realized that he had been wrong to suppose that he knew Stephen Lawlor. The Fascist badge in the stud box, the receipt from the Home of Mercy for the slum children of Dijon, the betrayal of Celia, the calm painting of a birth-mark on a dead man's body, the love of poetry, the charm, the gaiety, the good companionship—they were all unknowable.

The figure of Stephen Lawlor turned out of the public house into the street, and John Kevin, forcing his rioting thoughts into the back of his brain for future consideration, sped down the long bar in pursuit.

He was in deadly earnest now. Excitement, which had borne him along so bravely before, had given place to a grim, relentless determination; in a sense he knew that he was fighting for his life against a ruthless enemy. From that first dreamlike morning in Dublin until now, there had been a gradual strengthening of purpose, a strange, rather embarrassing sense of dedication. He knew now that the enemy was ruthless. Just how ruthless and how much an enemy he had yet to discover. At the moment he needed all his faculties for the job of pursuit.

He thought as he battled along, keeping Lawlor in sight, that it was a good thing the man had much on his mind; John Kevin knew that he was not an experienced stalker, and might be easily observed. But that was a risk he must take—only one, after all, among many others. This new determination stood him in good stead.

However, he nearly lost his quarry twice: once when the traffic of a main street barred pursuit, and once when Lawlor turned a corner and went into a shop. This latter incident was so sudden that Kevin nearly spoiled his whole plan by walking past the open door. Just in time he saw the danger and doubled back to the corner and safety. He had caught a glimpse, however, of the shop window, and it had contained dummy packets of cigarettes and cheap magazines; newspapers had flapped in a wire rack hung by the door. It seemed highly probable that this was the place which took messages for "Mr. Byrne." In that case they must be near the end of their journey. He was not sorry about this either; shadowing a man, he found, was exhausting and nerve-racking work. Perhaps luck was on his side, however, because not once did Lawlor look over his shoulder, and it was luck also, rather than judgment, which gave Kevin the cover of lunch hour; for the mean streets through which they went, and which half an hour earlier would have been deserted, were now thronged with workers emerging from some factory.

Indeed, the throng was so great at one moment that he nearly missed the point of all his trouble. Lawlor ran swiftly up the steps of a shabby grey house and let himself in with a latchkey. They had arrived, it appeared, at Number Five Macarthy Street. A small placard in a downstairs window advertised *Rooms to Let*.

Kevin knew exactly what he proposed to do, and he saw no point in wasting time. His plan, he fully realized, was far from foolproof, but it was the best he could make in the circumstances; it depended on shock tactics, on the very evident disquiet which Lawlor had shown at the mention of Mr. B. Tanner of Newcastle-on-Tyne, and on an entirely unknown quantity—to wit, the landlady at Number Five.

He went to the nearest telephone box, which, he was relieved to see, was round a corner, and dialed the number of Uncle Edward Dillon's house. To his added relief, but not to his surprise since it was customary, Finian answered.

"Now, listen," said Kevin, "this is very important, and not too easy. I want you to do something for me."

Finian replied that he was well above average intelligence.

"I'm going to give you a telephone number," Kevin went on. "I want you to ring it as soon as we've finished this conversation. Say that you have an urgent message for Mr. Byrne. Got that?"

Finian said that a child of six could do it.

"Right. Now, you must give a number for this Byrne to ring you back, and it mustn't be the phone you're on now."

Finian said that there was a café round the corner where he laid his bets; would that do?

"Perfectly. Can you wait there until he comes through? You can tell Mr. Dillon from me that it's vitally urgent."

Yes, Finian would do this.

"Now, when Mr. Byrne rings back, keep him in conversation as long as you can. Do it this way. Say you're a friend but that you won't give your name. Say that you got the number from another friend, a well-wisher, who thought it important that Mr. Byrne should know what you have to say. Then tell him this, taking as long as you can: tell him that there's a Mr. Kevin asking too many questions, and that you have every reason to believe that this Mr. Kevin is going to the police to tell all he knows. Embroider it as you like, but don't get too fantastic."

Finian replied with relish that he would embroider like a bard of old, and keep the man talking from now until doomsday. He added that Mr. Kevin was to take care of himself.

"All right, then," said Kevin. "Get going."

He left the telephone box and, making a detour by a parallel road, contrived to emerge at the opposite end of Macarthy Street. He didn't want to risk being seen by Lawlor. There was the inevitable public house on the corner; he went in, ordered a Guinness, and stared, ruminatively, he hoped, out of the window at Number Five.

He did not have very long to wait. A small boy presently appeared, ran up the steps and rang the doorbell. The door opened. The boy was voluble; then he handed over a slip of paper. The door closed. The boy scampered away. After a short pause Stephen Lawlor appeared at the top of the steps, ran down them and headed for the telephone box which Kevin had only recently vacated. As soon as he was out of view, Kevin left the public house and crossed the road to Number Five. He was trying hard to keep himself under control, but a desperate, driving urgency trembled inside him. Each second that the woman did not answer the doorbell seemed an eternity. When she finally appeared he only just managed to talk at a reasonable pace.

"May I speak to Mr. Byrne, please."

"You've just missed him," she said. "He went to the telephone a moment ago."

She was small, frail, birdlike. Any fear that he had felt concerning her implication in the business left him at once. He said, "Then I'll wait, for he won't be more than a few minutes."

His very words struck panic into his own heart; what if she should stay and chatter? Time was flying. He glanced at his watch—the whole manoeuvre so far had taken only ninety seconds. He must, must, must subdue this panic, or he would fail.

"Yes, by all means," she said. "But you'll excuse me. I have a pie in the oven." She turned away and then, maddeningly, back again. "His room's on the first floor, straight ahead. Perhaps you'd rather wait there— I mean if—if you're a friend, he won't mind."

"Oh, I'm a friend," replied Kevin, forcing what he knew must be a ghastly smile. He almost loved her for making it so easy.

She went back to the basement, and he, taking the stairs three at a time, leapt up to the first floor and into Stephen

Lawlor's room. The urgency was now like an evil eye on the small of his back—an omnipresent, terrifying panic which threatened to rob him of coherent action. He knew that if all he suspected was true, and Lawlor returned to find him, there would be no bungling of the death penalty this time. Wildly, but forcing himself to be neat, he searched dressing table and chest of drawers. Both, he was surprised to find, were all but empty.

As often as he dared spare time he glanced from the window towards the corner which hid the telephone box. Four minutes now. Finian was doing his job well. Four minutes, but no success in the search. The wardrobe proved equally barren, and damnably difficult to close. He cursed. Sweat was cold on his back; his hands trembled foolishly. He knelt and peered under the bed. A suitcase! Was that the front door? No. Why the hell hadn't he latched it from the inside?

If the suitcase had been locked he would have wept. It was not. He flung it open. Yes, it was packed ready for a journey; it explained all too well the empty drawers. He felt among the folded clothing for that shape he knew must be found. There was nothing. The pocket on the lid, then? His fingers touched something oblong and narrow among papers. He drew it out, and laughed a trifle hysterically. It was a passport. He flicked it open and was confronted with the picture of a man—and the man was wearing those same spectacles, owlish lenses, which he had seen on Stephen Lawlor!

In an ecstasy of hurry now, he stared fixedly at the face, memorizing it, and at the name and address written beneath: "Percy Norman Williamson. 2, The Drive. Elm Park. Wolverhampton."

Then he thrust the passport back into the pocket, closed the case, pushed it back under the bed, straightened up and took three paces to the door. As he closed it behind him, he heard for the second time that sound which ever afterwards would remind him of Dublin and of paralyzing fear —the sound of a latchkey being fitted into a lock. No time for the stairs now. And, glancing wildly round, he saw no place to hide—only doors behind which might lurk women ready to give him away with a scream. So, instead of going down, he went up the next flight of stairs, and the next. Below him in the hall the landlady's small voice said, "There was a gentleman to see you, Mr. Byrne. He's waiting in your room. I hope I . . ."

He heard Stephen Lawlor bound up the first flight and slam into his bedroom. The door closed and there was a still, nervous silence. Kevin was aware of a sudden access of courage; he knew, from wartime experience, that it came like this, seeming to be projected from outside the body. He was not in the habit of questioning it, and he did not do so now, but ran as lightly as he could—an absurd tiptoeing sprint—down the stairs, straight past Lawlor's room, across the hall and out of the house.

It was done. Unless he had erred completely in his argument, he now knew the name, and the address, of the man who had died on that secret, terrible night—the man whose body he had wrongly identified as Stephen Lawlor; the man who, unless here again he erred greatly, had been murdered *by* Stephen Lawlor in cold blood for a reason as yet unknown.

114

Kevin, walking back through the grey streets as fast as he could go without starting a hue and cry, knew that he had crossed his Rubicon and burned his boats. From now on it would be open warfare.

# V

As soon as he got back to Uncle Edward Dillon's house he ran up to his bedroom and wrote the name and address in his diary: "Percy Norman Williamson. 2, The Drive. Elm Park. Wolverhampton."

Then he went down to the library and, after some enquiry, succeeded in getting a call through to Inspector O'Connor.

"This is John Kevin," he said. "I've just remembered that I have an important appointment tomorrow in London. I suppose you've no objection to my going."

"Well," O'Connor replied, "in view of the circumstances of Mr. Lawlor's death . . ."

"I mean," said Kevin adroitly, "that there is no legal reason why I shouldn't go."

After a pause, O'Connor said, "No. None."

"Oh. Good. I shall be returning to Dublin, of course—and, in the meantime, you might care to have my London address." He did not add that there would be no one at his London address.

"Seventeen Pope Mews," echoed O'Connor. "West One.

You'll let me know when you get back here, won't you?"
He sounded most displeased.

Kevin said, "Of course." Then he rang off and dialed
the Aer Lingus number.

"My name is Williamson," he announced smoothly. "My
secretary booked a seat for me on one of your flights to
England. Unfortunately she made a mistake—or so I believe. She isn't here at the moment, so I wonder if I could
check up with you?"

"What," enquired an unsurprised voice, "would be your
destination?"

Kevin took a deep breath. "I have appointments in London, Glasgow and Birmingham—" he mentioned three of
the main Aer Lingus terminals—"but I'm afraid my secretary misunderstood the itinerary. I'm sorry to be so vague;
it's most irritating."

The voice said, "One moment, please," in a tone which
indicated that it often had to deal with nincompoops.
Presently it returned to say, "We have a booking for this
evening on our Flight E1240 in the name of Mr. P. N.
Williamson. The destination is Glasgow. Time of departure, six-twenty from the City Air Terminal, seven-ten
from the airport."

"Ah," said Kevin. "Thank you very much."

"Do you wish a cancellation, sir?"

He considered for a moment the possibility of preventing
Stephen Lawlor from leaving the country; it was not, he
decided, a sensible course of action. Therefore he said,
"No, that's quite all right. The booking is perfectly correct. I'm so sorry to have troubled you."

"Not at all, sir," replied the voice, justifiably weary at

117

this waste of its valuable time. (Kevin's opinion of the Aer Lingus staff—already high—rose yet higher.)

So Lawlor's packed suitcase was no general precaution; he intended to leave Eire for Glasgow. Why, Kevin wondered, Glasgow?

He was still pondering this when the library door opened and Uncle Edward Dillon walked in. Kevin stood up, smiling, but he noticed at once an unusual weariness in the old gentleman's bearing. "Ah," he said, "so you're back. I'm glad."

"Why, sir? Is— Is anything the matter?"

Edward Dillon replaced a book neatly on its shelf and turned to regard the young man. "You look tired," he said, but he held up a hand to prevent Kevin from speaking. "No. As I've said before I refuse to be enlightened. I won't say I'm not curious. I am. But I've reached the age when secrets are tedious—especially the secrets of the young. That's not what I wanted to see you about."

"I've never thanked you properly," said Kevin, "for your hospitality . . ."

Uncle Edward shook his head. "No, nor that either. Hospitality is always a pleasure. It's Celia—" He hesitated.

"Celia?"

The old man nodded; he looked very unhappy suddenly. "I think," he said, "that you must go and talk to her. She is very young, and when one is old—" He wavered helplessly. "Out of touch, you know. Not surprising. Stopped living a long time ago, as it happens." He made a sad gesture, embracing the inevitability of age. "*You* go and talk to her, there's a good boy."

"But what's the matter?"

"Oh, heavens above, what indeed? That damned Lawlor fellow, I suppose. She was fond of him—no doubt about that. The women of our family are loyal, you know, loyal through thick and thin. So far she's been all right; unhappy, mind you, but all right. Now—" Again he gestured.

"Now what?" enquired Kevin, heavy at heart.

"Locked in her room. No lunch. Won't see anybody."

"Damn Stephen Lawlor," said Kevin fiercely.

"Agreed. Certainly. God rest his soul." Uncle Edward opened the door and held it so. Kevin sighed, braced himself, and walked out into the hall and upstairs.

It was a long time before Celia opened the door and let him in—approximately an hour after his first attempt. He entered bearing a tray of sandwiches and coffee which Finian, greatly distressed, had prepared for them both.

She flung herself back onto the bed, where, from the look of it, she had been lying for some hours.

"Well," said Kevin, "here's food. And let me say at the outset I'm doing this because your uncle asked me to."

She did not reply, but her back, as he had discovered at their first meeting, was very eloquent. Now, as then, it moved him to a deep pity. He could do nothing, however —and he could say nothing, either. He put the tray on her bedside table, poured himself out a cup of coffee, took two sandwiches on a plate, and sat down. After a time, a long time, he said, "It's no good my offering sympathy, because it does no good—not to people like you or me. Some people seem to like it—" He left that in midair. He felt deeply, almost painfully, sorry for her. He hated himself almost as much as he hated Stephen Lawlor.

119

Later he said, "I was spoiled by the war—for death, I mean. It doesn't mean as much as it used to."

Then, surprisingly, she rolled over and looked at him. He had half-expected to see her face blotchy with weeping, but in this he had misjudged her; it was ravaged by a grief more bitter than mere tears. She stared at him with dark, curiously unblinking eyes. Her voice, when she spoke, was deeper than he remembered. Weary.

She said, "You're quite a person, aren't you? I—I think I owe you an apology. It never does to take anybody for granted. No one . . . No one is quite what they seem, are they?" After a time, she added, "God knows, I should have learnt that."

She swung her legs off the bed, stood up and went across to the dressing table. There she sat down and examined her face in the mirror, dispassionately, with an expression of utter boredom.

"It's funny," she said finally. "I never wept for Stephen dead. But for Stephen alive I wept an hour on end. More fool me."

She must have seen his expression of utter incredulity in the looking glass, for she added, "I heard you make that appointment on the phone this morning. I—I followed you. I saw him."

Kevin said, "Oh, dear God!"

"No." She turned. "Don't be horrified. I asked for it, didn't I?" She contrived a laugh. "What an idiot I must have seemed to you, thinking he loved me. Love!" She smacked her bare palm onto the glass top of the table. "Love!" she said again. "And he let me think he was dead. He let me suffer like that."

Kevin stood up. "I'd have told you if I—if I'd thought it would help at all. I just couldn't bring myself to do it."

She caught his eye in the mirror. "And, surely, he asked you not to?"

"Yes, he did."

"And you're loyal, too, aren't you?" Thus quickly and certainly she struck to the heart of the matter—struck to the heart of Stephen Lawlor's betrayal of them both.

"Listen . . ." he began.

"*No!*" She almost shouted it. "I've had as much as I can stand. Don't try to explain—not yet. I couldn't bear it." After a moment, in a flat, dead voice, she added, "But don't think I can't see the implications. He didn't die, but somebody did—and for a good reason, too, I've no doubt."

He knew there was nothing more he could say immediately. He left her sitting there, gazing with a kind of incredulous distaste at her own reflection. He knew that feeling well. There were times when it seemed impossible that one could live a moment longer with the pathetic idiot which was oneself.

Kevin felt in some way freed by her discovery. He had, it was true, already decided to go to Wolverhampton and delve into the identity of Percy Norman Williamson; in fact, it would have taken a lot to stop him. On the other hand, although he knew that what she was now suffering was far more painful than her grief at Lawlor's death, he had not relished the idea of leaving her alone with the lie.

Now that she knew the truth he felt he could devote himself entirely to the problem which faced him. Who was Williamson? How had he been connected with Stephen Lawlor? And why had it been necessary for him to die? Kevin was eager to get to Wolverhampton. (An unusual state of affairs, since on his only visit there he had vowed never again to set foot in the place.) He was eager to leave Dublin.

Fortunately Aer Lingus had a seat for him on their 6:15 flight to Birmingham. He went straight to the City Air Terminal, collected his ticket, and then made his way to the chemist in Grafton Street.

The photograph of the rat-faced man at the hotel was not particularly good; but it could, at a later date, be scientifically clarified if that became necessary. Perhaps, when the matter of Percy Norman Williamson had been forced to make sense, the photograph might be useful. Kevin was sure, though he could not have said why, that in the end he would have to return to Dublin; that everything —the Tara Lounge, the attempts to end his life, the mystery of the man who had died—would lead him back inevitably to this beautiful, yet somehow sinister, city.

He did not even pause to think how completely he had become involved in so fantastic an affair. It was a personal matter now, and his dislike of Lawlor was a personal enmity. Nothing could stop him pursuing it to its conclusion.

There was only one other stray end which he did not like to leave hanging in midair, and that was the United Freedom Movement. He was still curious about this institution, although he felt it to be a side issue, and he very much wanted to know how and why Stephen Lawlor was connected with it.

Since he had plenty of time at his disposal, he decided to make his way back to Edward Dillon's house via Antrim

Street and the Movement's headquarters. In this decision he was lucky, for as he turned down that distressing Victorian vista and drew level with Number 144, he glanced up and beheld a quite unmistakable figure approaching. The arms flapped as he walked, giving him less the appearance of a vulture than of an alarmed hen riding its flight with absurd wings; he appeared to be talking to himself, and he stared fixedly at the ground two yards in front of his feet. It was the Merrion Square apparition. Kevin prepared himself for another fantastic encounter.

When the man was approximately two yards away his gaze encountered Kevin's feet. He stopped dead and looked up. His eyes widened astonishingly and his mouth opened.

So, thought Kevin, I was not wrong in tracing this odd character to the doorstep of United Freedom; I was probably not wrong either in supposing that he met Stephen Lawlor here.

He said, "You remember me, surely? A friend of Mr. Lawlor's. Kevin's the name."

The man stared. He now looked, Kevin thought, like a chicken whose neck had just been wrung. Clearly he was astounded, shocked out of his wits.

"I'd like to talk to you," Kevin said, "about our late friend. Perhaps you could help me." And he took a step forward. Whereupon the man performed a sudden and astonishing balletic sideways leap, emitting as he did so a hen's alarmed squawk; he clattered down the area steps, nearly falling the last three, opened the door, and vanished, slamming it behind him. A key turned in the lock.

Kevin stared, astonished but laughing in spite of himself.

The face appeared presently at a basement window. It

gazed up at the young man who leaned, laughing, on the area railings. And suddenly it no longer looked like a scared chicken, but like a vulture again. There was something evil and watchful about the expression; it almost gloated.

Kevin, from laughter, felt that flicker of fear in the small of his back. And he walked away quickly.

Celia had left the seclusion of her bedroom. She and Uncle Edward were having tea in the library when Kevin got back. He was astonished by her self-control; no casual observer would ever have known what was in her thoughts. Except that her eyes were tired and that, in some subtle way, she looked older than before, there was no indication of what she had suffered, and was still suffering.

When Kevin joined them she was standing behind her uncle's chair. Their eyes met, and she shook her head gently, indicating that she had said nothing to the old gentleman of their afternoon's conversation.

Kevin took the cup of tea which she offered him and said, "I hope you won't think it very sudden of me, but I'm flying to England tonight."

The girl stared fixedly while her uncle and the young man satisfied their social consciences. Kevin was aware of the stare, and he found it unsettling. She said little during the rest of tea; but as soon as he went to his bedroom to pack, she followed, as he had been sure she would.

Closing the door and leaning on it, she said, "I'm coming, too."

Without looking up from his suitcase he replied, "No. Stay here. You may be useful."

124

She came round the bed to face him. "Where are you going?"

"Birmingham."

"Why? What have you discovered?"

"Nothing. Yet."

After a pause she said, "You don't trust me, do you?"

He straightened. "We've agreed to differ, haven't we? I've told you that I intend to dig down to the bottom of this business, however dirty it proves to me. I meant what I said." He folded a suit with practiced neatness. "I understand perfectly why you don't want me to do so. But that isn't going to stop me."

"No," she said, wonderingly. "You wouldn't let that stop you." She seemed faintly surprised.

"It's not only the personal angle," he went on. "There's more to it than that. I don't know what's behind it yet, but something is—something dirty. I—I can feel it."

He looked rather helpless suddenly, caught up in this thing which he could feel, but which he could not express in words. She watched him for a long time in silence. Then she said, "You're crusading, do you know that?"

"Possibly. What's wrong with crusading?"

"Nothing. I rather admire you for it; it's rare. To be quite frank I didn't think you had it in you."

He grinned, suddenly boyish. "I'm a mass of contradictions."

"I'd like to come with you," she said again. "And don't say I'll be *useful* here. It's a downright lie, and you know it. You don't trust me, why not be honest?"

"No." His grey eyes met her brown eyes in a straight stare. "You're dead right, I don't trust you. I'm going ahead with this thing and I don't want you at my elbow whispering at me to give up all the time."

Still staring, she said, "I couldn't influence you one way or the other. You're too damned obstinate."

"You might." He smiled. "I'm terribly susceptible to feminine charm."

He watched her colour at this, and it struck him as he did so that she was, in fact, rather a beautiful creature; so self-possessed, so cool, so complete unto herself, and yet possessing that air of grave childishness—a grave and beautiful air of innocence.

He was aware, too, of the fact that she was trying to say something—something difficult, perhaps even humiliating, which she in her great honesty knew must be said. In this, however, she failed. He saw the light die in her face, and she shrugged, suddenly weary again. Then she turned and walked out of the room.

He was hurt, when the time came for him to go, to find that she had left the house without even waiting to say good-by. Perhaps he had deserved it, but all the same it hurt. He brooded over it in the bus which carried him from the City Air Terminal to the airport. He told himself that he was being a great deal *too* susceptible to feminine charm; he told himself that he was behaving like an idiot. But still, in spite of self-instruction, it hurt.

In this mood, he snapped at the Customs officer who asked him if he had anything to declare; and, as a result, the Customs officer made him open all his luggage and was suspicious about the three cameras. They were cordially rude to each other.

The luggage was whisked away to the waiting airliner,

and Kevin went straight to the bar, conveniently placed in a corner of the Customs room. He growled at the barmaid, who, as a result, answered back pertly. He was hurt. He was like the proverbial bear with a sore ear; he looked on nobody and at nothing; he couldn't have cared less; he drank a couple of double whiskies and was hurt.

In this way, it was not until they had been ushered out to the waiting plane—it was not until he had taken his seat and fastened the safety belt—it was not until the door had been closed and the engines were revving up that he saw Celia sitting two places away on the other side of the gangway.

Paradoxically, instead of being furiously angry, he was swept by a wave of pleasure; the hurt vanished abruptly, and he was momentarily ashamed about the pleasant young Customs officer and the pretty barmaid.

The seat next to her was empty. As soon as they had taken off, he loosened his safety belt and went and sat down in it. She glanced sideways, and the glance told him that whatever her opinion of his capabilities she was not above being afraid of him. But he was so pleased to see her that he could only grin excitedly. It was an infectious grin, and she caught it at once.

"Hell," he said. "What does it matter? Have a drink?"

The coast of Ireland slipped away beneath them. Looking at her profile, so calm and yet so touchingly young, he was struck by a pang of misgiving. "Listen," he said, "we're heading for an unknown quantity. There may be danger—there *will* be danger. I don't want you to—"

He broke off, staring in amazement. She had felt in her bag, and now, resting on the palm of her hand, lay a re-

127

volver—no mother-of-pearl-butted toy either—a Colt .38. "Uncle Edward's," she said calmly. "I borrowed it."

Kevin gaped, and the air hostess, catching sight of it as she arrived with the drinks, nearly dropped her tray.

*part three:* **RUDE AWAKENING**

—————————— **I**

Number Two, The Drive, Elm Park, Wolverhampton, also bore a name upon its gate. The name was "Arcadia." It struck an incongruous note in the ugly street of red brick set in a wilderness of suburbia—endless, endless suburbia. Kevin had hired a self-drive car in Birmingham, and it seemed that they had been wending their way all morning through serried, characterless hinterlands of small houses.

He had left Celia sitting in the car because he suspected that the approaching interview—if his theory was correct—might prove not only involved but harrowing. Now he stared at "Arcadia," and "Arcadia" stared back—one of a row of seventy identical semidetached horrors.

*Et in Wolverhampton ego* . . . thought Kevin, and was sad.

He pulled himself together and opened the gate, which had a high-pitched, tooth-grating squeak. Somewhere inside Number Two a dog barked. Dogs in Numbers One and Four—"Iona" and "The Lilacs" respectively—began to bark also.

Kevin rapped on the door. Above it was a stained-glass window depicting lilies and clover, of all unlikely mixtures, in a William Morris entanglement.

Here levity ended. The door was opened by a fat and very unhappy woman. And the terrible thing was that there was hope in her eyes.

"Yes?" she said breathlessly.

"Mrs. Williamson?"

"Yes. Is it—?" Her lower lip trembled, and Kevin knew that he hated Stephen Lawlor very much indeed; a blind hatred for that callous man overwhelmed him. He did not need to ask if Percy Norman Williamson was missing; the mother's face told him all that and more.

"Is it about Percy?" she said.

"In a way, yes."

"Is he all right? Have you seen him?"

Luckily for Kevin a man now appeared—a small, bald man with a pale face on which spectacles sat crushingly. He said, "Now, Ma, it's no good getting worked up. You'll only make yourself ill." In spite of his smallness he had a firm, comforting voice. He ushered Kevin into a sitting room, which on another occasion would have reduced him to helpless wonder, and sat him down in a red plush armchair. Kevin stared stupidly at the windowsill on which reposed a dreadful plaster figurine of a small girl making a daisy chain. He was hating every minute of this.

Little Mr. Williamson said, "Well?" and he knew he must speak. Their hopefulness was heart-rending.

"Are you a friend of Percy's?" demanded the woman, almost suspiciously.

Kevin took a deep breath. "No," he said. "I'm not."

"You saw the bit in 'The News of The World,' " said the man.

"Yes." Kevin seized on this. "You see, I've been on holiday in Dublin and I met a fellow called Williamson in a bar one evening. And I wondered, when I saw the name in 'The News of The World' . . ." He supposed that there had been a mention in that paper's missing people's column. He knew that he must feel his way carefully or he would find himself having to answer the police.

"What was he like?" said the woman breathlessly. "It's not an unusual name—a good name— mind you, but not unusual."

Kevin recalled the passport photograph. "Well, he wore glasses. We only spoke a few words and I didn't notice much else. Quite a tall fellow."

"Glasses!" Mr. Williamson leaned forward.

"Yes. Odd ones, with very strong lenses . . ."

The woman sobbed, and held a handkerchief to her mouth. "It's him," she said. "That's him. I can feel it in my bones, Harold."

"But in Dublin—" said the man. "He didn't know anybody in Ireland."

"Such a *quiet* boy," added the mother. "He didn't have many friends, not even here at home."

Kevin thought quickly. "There was another man with him," he said. "I was introduced. Name was Lawlor."

Their faces were quite blank.

"A good-looking fellow with an Irish accent."

Mr. Williamson shook his head wearily. "No. You see, our Percy is a very quiet boy, Mr.—er—"

Kevin said, "Scott."

"Mr. Scott. He's a home-loving boy. Not very go-ahead maybe, but a good son."

"He *likes* his home," said fat Mrs. Williamson through her handkerchief. "What's wrong in that, may I ask?"

"Nothing, nothing," said her husband soothingly. "I was just trying to explain to Mr.—to Mr. Scott here that our Percy wasn't likely to be in a bar in Dublin."

"But he *was* in a bar in Dublin," she wailed, suddenly in tears. "He was. How many—boys d'you see wearing spectacles like Percy's? He *was* in Dublin." She sobbed openly now. "It's some woman, that's what it is."

"Oh, Ma," said the little man wearily, "talk sense, there's a dear. Perce hardly ever looks at a girl."

"He looked at that Mavis Brooks," declared Mrs. Williamson with feeling. In spite of her grief Kevin found himself beginning to dislike her.

Perhaps her husband felt the same way. He said, "Now, dear, how about making Mr. Scott and me a nice cup of tea, eh? I'm sure Mr. Scott would like a cup of tea."

Rather unwillingly she agreed to this suggestion and withdrew, snuffling.

The two men looked at each other.

"She's upset," said Mr. Williamson. "She gets upset easily. Is— Is there anything else you'd like to tell me—now that we're alone, I mean?"

Kevin could see no possible connection between Percy Williamson, the quiet boy who liked his home, and Stephen Lawlor—the unquiet boy with no home. He avoided this question, therefore, and said, "You seem very sure your son wouldn't go to Ireland. Maybe it wasn't him I met, after all."

134

"Yes," said the little man. "I think it was him, Mr. er— Scott. I didn't say so in front of the wife, but I think it was him. What he's up to, I can't imagine."

"Surely he might go without telling you?"

"Ah." The man sighed. "You don't know our Percy. He's quiet, Mr. Scott. A nice book or his wireless set— that's all he wants of an evening. No girls, no dancing— doesn't even like football. Doesn't even do the pools."

There was something in this picture which was not quite satisfying; it nagged at the outside edges of Kevin's brain.

"Mind you," said Percy's father, "he's no youngster. We say our 'boy,' but, of course, he's a man of thirty."

If he had been a boy, Kevin thought bitterly—if he hadn't been about the same age and build as Stephen Lawlor—he might be alive now. But what, in heaven's name, was the connection? Percy Williamson. Stephen Lawlor. Where did they touch?

"Even the Army didn't make much difference to our Perce," said Mr. Williamson. "He got on well enough with the other boys, you know, but he didn't seem to get what you might call friendly with any of them. Funny lad." Clearly the man was bewildered by his own son. "Not like our Charlie, but he was killed in the Air Force, was Charlie. He was a gay spark, I can tell you." And the tired eyes were alight for a moment at the memory of Charlie.

"Have you been to the police about your son's disappearance?" said Kevin, to whom Charlie was of no interest. (He had known too many Air Force "gay sparks" in his time—and they were tedious.)

"The police!" snapped Mr. Williamson. "We told 'em

135

Perce was on holiday and wasn't due home till tomorrow, and they said he'd turn up soon enough when he had to go back to work. Said they'd had over two hundred enquiries from parents who didn't know where their children had gone on holiday. He couldn't see that it wasn't like our Perce at all."

"Where does he work, Mr. Williamson?"

"General Post Office. Engineer." Evidently he was proud of this. "Oh, yes, he's got a good job, has Percy. Well, the Army trained him for it, you see—wireless and all that—and he liked the work, so he went right ahead when he was demobbed."

Mrs. Williamson reappeared with the tea tray. "Of course, he went right ahead," she butted in. "He's a clever boy, is Percy—and a good son. And that's why he wouldn't go away and not write."

"Now, Ma," said her husband.

"And as soon as you've had your cup of tea I'm putting on my hat and going straight down to give that police sergeant a bit of my mind." She breathed heavily, her massive bosom rising and falling.

Oh, God, thought Kevin, his hopes tumbling about him, what connection? What possible connection?

Almost any other kind of person would have had more chance of meaning something to Stephen Lawlor. But Percy Norman Williamson, "our Perce," had to be the one in question: quiet, unassuming, no friends, no interests—just a book by the fire and a wireless set. Damnation!

"Surely," he said, "your son might have gone to Ireland with a friend?"

The man shook his head.

"It'll be a woman," said Mrs. Williamson. "You see."

"No," said her husband. "He only had one friend—they do the wireless together."

Kevin sat up straight suddenly. The doubt which had been nagging at the edges of his brain was clear to him suddenly.

"Wireless?" he said. "You mean your son makes a hobby of it?"

"Oh, *yes*," said the proud parents together, and Mr. Williamson added, "A rare dab at wireless, our Perce. Built their own set, him and Stan did—Stan's his friend."

Mrs. Williamson sniffed.

"A transmitter, mind you," said her husband. "No easy job building a transmitter. Oh, yes, Perce is a dab at radio. Took his exam the other day, too."

Of course, Kevin was thinking. "Our Perce" couldn't conceivably have been as dull as his mother and father made him. He had to have that hobby—that one devouring passion. Yes, amateur wireless; it fitted exactly. It was the one outstanding thing about Percy Norman Williamson. It might be . . . It *must* be the connecting link.

He was excited now. He said, "Can I see the wireless, please?"

The attic was a wild jumble of wire, pieces of paper, old valves, technical magazines and empty lemonade bottles. Mrs. Williamson, peering in at the mess, tut-tutted fondly.

"He never lets me in here," she explained. "Says he won't be able to find anything if I tidy it up. He's a caution, is Perce."

Kevin stared round at the confusion with an exasperated

frown. Here might be the connection; here it *must* be. But where the devil should he start looking for it?

Mr. Williamson pushed his large spectacles up onto his forehead. "It's all a mystery to me," he admitted. Clearly both of them thought it strange that he should want to see the room. Presently, Kevin realized, Mrs. Williamson would begin to ask suspicious questions—and they weren't going to be easy to answer. What reason *could* he give for his interest that would not seem to them odd? He made an attempt to forestall them.

"I thought," he said, "that maybe we could find some sort of clue here. I mean as to why he went to Ireland."

The Williamsons looked doubtful.

But the clue *is* here, Kevin thought angrily. He stared round the untidy room, and was reminded of the Tara Lounge—of how he had stood there by the bar, staring around, willing the place to reveal its secret. This attic, like the Tara Lounge, revealed nothing. It was stolidly inanimate.

Regardless of their suspicious eyes he began to examine the transmitter, the workbench, the magazines. Evidently "our Perce" was a Morse devotee. Pages and pages of paper were scribbled over with odd scraps of messages in plain language or in code. They lay in heaps on the table and on the floor; they lay, mixed up with obscure calculations and even more obscure electrical diagrams, on the workbench, on the chairs, and between the pages of the magazines. Kevin began to have a healthy respect for "our Perce"; he was clearly, as his father had said, "a dab at radio."

But to the nontechnical eye it was all meaningless. There

might, in this mess, be any number of clues staring him in the face. Or, on the other hand, there might be none. It was infuriating.

Mrs. Williamson was by now openly suspicious. Unless he wanted to answer some exceedingly awkward questions he knew that the time had come to go. And then, as he turned to speak, something caught his eye. One of the messages, more legible than the rest, lay face upward on top of the transmitter—and he saw that the first group read *DJ121*.

For a moment, though a chord was struck in his memory, Kevin could not catch and pigeonhole the connection. It was like a forgotten name hovering on the tip of the tongue. Evasive. Maddening.

And then he remembered. Among the Parisian telephone numbers and the train times in the back of his diary, Stephen Lawlor had jotted down those two letters followed by those three figures: *DJ121*.

Here, then, was the connecting link.

Celia said, "I don't get it."

They were driving once more between the endless rows of red-brick houses.

"No," Kevin admitted. "Neither do I. But Stan may."

Celia glanced at him. "And who is Stan?"

"Our Perce's chum. Luckily I got his address out of them before Ma Williamson started her private-detective line. Do I *look* like a private detective?"

"I've never met one, but I shouldn't think so." After a pause she said, "It must have been—rather horrible. Talking to them, I mean, and all the time knowing that he—that he's dead."

"It was at first. The old man'll be cut up when he hears. As for Ma—"

"What?"

"I got a nasty feeling," said Kevin, "that she'll just love all the publicity—better than a nice funeral."

Celia looked at him, at the brown face which always looked boyish and uncomplicated. "You say the nastiest things sometimes."

"Yes, I do, don't I?"

They drove in silence after that. Later she said, "You know, I'm getting a terrible sort of clinical interest in this business. It's not very nice, really. Morbid."

Kevin grunted.

"And the odd thing is that although I want to know what lies behind it, I—I still don't want Stephen to—to come to any harm."

Kevin said, "We differ on that point then. I hope they hang him."

She glanced at him, then, as she had done on the plane: a look almost of fear.

"Cedar Road," he added, looking out of the window. "Stan lives at Number Nineteen. His name's Ponsonby, by the way, and there isn't a hope in hell of seeing him now because he's sure to be out at work. We might catch him in his lunch hour, I thought. Nineteen, there it is."

Celia, watching him ring the doorbell, wondered for the hundredth time what had made her catch that plane from Dublin, and why—here and now—she was sitting in this car watching this rather fierce, sometimes alarming young

140

man leaning on the doorbell of Number Nineteen, Cedar
Road.

She could not even now think of Stephen Lawlor without a pang. It was not a thing of the mind at all—with her
mind she knew that she could never bear to be in the same
room with him again. It was a fierce physical blow just
above the heart. His eyes had narrowed when he smiled,
and small wrinkles puckered at the outsides of them; and
the shape of his mouth was so clearly, beautifully defined—
so hard that the lips might have been cut in stone, and yet
so surprisingly soft, though firm, when he had kissed her.
And at the memory of his kissing, the pain in her breast
was almost too fierce to bear.

Kevin, returning to the car, saw once again how her
face was ravaged by that secret misery. He put his hand
over hers in a gesture of sympathy.

"Time," he said, "that's the thing. It's insulting but it's
true. Time really does heal everything."

She nodded, blinking. "How can a person be so cruel?"
she said. "He didn't *seem* a cruel man."

"No, he didn't. Perhaps that's the cruellest thing of all."

He pressed the starter, and slipped into gear.

Celia, somewhat to her surprise, found that he had
soothed her; his presence was in some way reassuring and
solid—the last thing she had expected it to be. It struck
her suddenly that, subconsciously, this could have been the
reason that she had caught the plane with him; this, and
the fact that she could not bear to be left alone with her
thoughts. Something—she sensed it now—was driving her
on to whatever the end of Stephen Lawlor might be. She
understood, quite suddenly, just why this fair, surprising

141

young man beside her was determined to get at the truth. He felt himself to be involved too deeply for retraction; he would never rest unless he had done what he took to be his duty in this matter. She had called him a Crusader, half-mocking him. Now she saw that the name really did apply. It made him admirable in a way, but also stupid. He felt that he must pursue the truth, for his own peace of mind. And that, with variations, was her feeling, too. It astonished her; it did more—she was shocked.

"We are going," said Kevin, "to Bert's Caff in Vale End. I hope you're very hungry, you'll probably need to be."

"Is that where Stan lunches?"

"Apparently. He's some sort of mechanic. He works at a big engineering place called Morton's. I hope to heaven he's talkative."

"Bert's Caff" was exactly what Kevin had expected: a large, bare room crowded with small tables and hard, battered chairs. At one end was a counter where you ordered your food from a sallow feminine face entrenched behind piles of meat pies, several wheezing tea urns and cards advertising minerals.

Celia appropriated a corner table while Kevin fetched two large platefuls of bacon, chips and tomatoes, two cups of tea, and two plates of bread and butter.

"How shall we recognize him?" she asked, when he had set down his load and settled himself beside her.

"His mother tells me that he wears a red and black tartan shirt and blue overalls, and that he goes to his lunch at twelve-thirty sharp. If we don't spot him we'll start asking questions. Someone here's bound to know him by name."

But they did spot him; his shirt was unmistakable, and

142

could have been seen a mile away given good visibility. He had rather an engaging face with bright, merry eyes, an upturned nose and jet-black curly hair. He joined them at their table, subjected Celia to an appreciative examination and said, "Well, don't mind my asking, but what's old Perce to you?" His tone was affectionately mocking. He was clearly a different proposition altogether to Percy Norman Williamson.

Kevin, taking the line of least resistance, explained that he had seen the description of Williamson in the missing people's column of "The News of The World," recognized a man he had met in Dublin, and reacted accordingly. It was a loose lie, and he could see at once that it did not absolutely satisfy Stan Ponsonby; he took it, however, at its face value.

"His ma and pa," said Stan, "well, they're a shaky pair, you know. Flew into a panic as soon as he didn't show up at Blackpool."

"Blackpool?"

"Yes. Said he was going there for his holiday. Perce in Blackpool!" He grinned. "I'd like to see it."

Kevin said, "Where did you think he'd gone?"

"He's vague, is old Perce. And between you and me he gets a bit tired of his ma's fussing. I think he popped off somewhere quiet on his own; if you saw him in Dublin, then Dublin it is. Nothing strange in that. His ma and pa should've kept their heads instead of flying off in a panic. He'll be back tomorrow in time to go to work. You see." He stared at them with bright, intelligent eyes.

"So," Kevin said, "you've no idea what might have taken him to Dublin?"

Mr. Ponsonby took a mouthful of meat pie. Then he said, "No idea at all." But there was, behind the nonchalance, a subtle suggestion of uneasiness. It told Kevin what he wanted to know. The man was hiding something.

They all ate in silence for a time.

"Why?" said Stan eventually. "Do *you* know what might have taken him to Dublin?"

"I'm not sure."

There was another silence. The young man's disquiet was more apparent now; clearly he found the silences trying. Kevin waited until he felt that they were reaching the breaking point of suppressed uneasiness. Then, very gently, he said, "And how about DJ121?"

The young man froze, a forkful of pie arrested in midair between his plate and his mouth. After a moment he lowered the fork. His eyes were very intent, wary. There was an even longer, even more pregnant silence.

"Look," Kevin said. "I know just what's biting you, and there's nothing I can say to *prove* that we're trustworthy. We are, but I can't prove it."

Stan nodded, masticating slowly.

Kevin went on. "I've no doubt you promised Williamson that you'd keep quiet about whatever it is you know. Correct?"

"Correct," said Stan.

"And I've got a damn good reason for keeping quiet about what I know, too—a better reason than a promise. See what I mean?"

"Sort of."

"Then I'll put it plainly. We've got to trust each other or we'll get nowhere."

"You start by trusting me," replied Stan warily.

"We've got to trust *each other*," said Kevin again with emphasis.

"Tell me one thing—" Stan leaned forward. "Just why are you so keen to know about Perce and Dublin?"

Their eyes met and held—both determined, both aware of the thin ice of mistrust beneath them. Kevin sensed that it was a case of now or never; he knew character when he met it, and Stan had character. He was aware that he took a grave risk, but aware also that only this risk might work the trick. He said, "Your chum Percy is dead."

The young man's eyes widened; he put his fork down with a clatter. Then, after a moment, when the shock had passed, he said, "And can you prove *that*, mister?"

Kevin shook his head. He was beginning to feel desperate before this extreme wariness. "No, of course I can't prove it."

"There's been nothing in the papers."

"Yes, there has—but they thought he was somebody else."

Stan said, "Where do you come in?"

"That's a long story; but someone's tried to kill me, too— that's what I meant when I said I had a good reason for keeping quiet."

"You mean someone *killed* old Perce?"

"They did."

"Strewth!" Stan looked from Kevin's earnest face to Celia's—no less earnest—and back again. It was evident now that he wanted to trust them, but could not bring himself to break his word to Percy Williamson.

It was chance—one of those haphazard, unreasonable chances that tipped the scales. Kevin said, "Listen, the chap was your oppo, I appreciate that, but can't you see . . ."

"Oppo?" said Stan. "Were you in the Navy, too?"

"I was—for five long years."

Stan grinned abruptly. "Me, too."

This seemed in some odd way to decide him. It was not, admittedly, a very solid decisive factor, but destinies have been changed by flimsier ones than that.

"All right," said Stan, "I'll tell you."

Stan took a gulp of tea and said, "Mind you, I don't know Perce very well. He's a dull sort of chap, really, but he's darn good on radio and I like messing about with it myself. That's how we met, you see—at the Radio Club.

"Mind you, I've got lots of other interests too, but, old Perce, he's a rare stick-in-the-mud. Radio, radio, radio—that's all he wants. Him and me's oppos all right, but only over the wireless, so to speak. Sometimes I've tried to make him come to the pictures or a football match, but oh, no—not old Perce. He stays home with his blessed set.

"Once or twice he's got real mad at me because I won't go and help him with it some evening when I've got another date. Called me a dilly—dilly-whatnot. You know."

"Dilettante."

"That's right. 'Well,' I said, 'maybe I am. Maybe I do like girls, too. You can't marry a radio set—it'd be damn uncomfortable to go to bed with, anyway.'" He glanced apprehensively at Celia. "Sorry. Where was I?" He brooded for a moment in silence. "Funny old cove, Perce.

"Well, about three months ago I went round to help him rig a new aerial. It was Sunday, see, and I remember telling him he looked just about fagged out—he did too. I asked him what he'd been up to. He said he'd been awake all night. 'Lumme,' I said, 'what doing?' 'Reading Morse,' says Perce and he shuts up like a clam. But he was—he was sort of excited, all the same.

"Of course, his ma was in a dizzy about it, saying he'd ruin his health and all the rest of it.

"Sometimes," said Stan ruminatively, "I wondered whether old Perce wasn't a bit balmy.

"Well, anyway, that was the beginning of it. Up till then his little room in the attic had been as clean as you like. When I went there next it was a bloody shambles—sorry, miss, but it was. Paper all over the place. And old Perce, he looked as though he'd spent a couple of weeks in Sister Street." He glanced at Celia, noted that the allusion had gone over her head, and continued.

"Fair whacked he looked. Well, of course, he'd been sitting up night after night, see. It was plain as a pikestaff. And the whole place was covered in signals—messages."

He leaned forward.

"And every one of them started off with that DJ121."

"Code or plain language?"

"Ah, that was it. Code, the whole blinkin' lot—except for acknowledgments and reception signals and a few short ones that didn't mean much."

"Such as?"

Stan thought for a moment. "Well, one of them said, 'Tell Harry to get a move on!' I remember that. Oh yes, and one said, 'Peter is going home. Tell the others.' That sort of thing.

"Well, I knew old Perce. It was obvious he thought he was onto something. I buttered him up a bit, and presently he talked. Not much, mind you—he was always a close, old so-and-so—but enough for me to get the hang of what he was up to.

"Seems that one time in the Army Perce did a bit of cipher work, and he'd got the idea that it's only common sense that's needed to break down an ordinary straightforward code. Not the classy ones that change every day, mind you—just ordinary ones.

"Well, now, this DJ121 business had apparently been using the same code for ages. Business firms and so on don't change them often, you know—too much trouble.

"Perce's theory was that if you read enough messages you soon begin to see light. Take the word *the*, for instance—or *and*—well, they're bound to occur pretty often, aren't they? And old Perce argued that you could soon pick out the three letters, or the group, that were substituted for them in the code. Trial and error, of course.

"Mind you, it's the sort of thing'd drive me round the bend, but not old Perce. And he had some other theory, too, I couldn't begin to understand, about the frequency of identical digits. Don't ask *me* what he meant because I don't know. I reckon if Perce had had a university education he'd have been in atom bombs. A clever sort of old beaver, our Perce.

"Well, he showed me in practice what he meant. He said he'd explain it with a simple letter code; he said if you once got *the* and *and* placed, that gave you six letters in the code. *T*, *h*, *e*, *a*, *n* and *d*. From those six you began to build up other words. He worked out a *t*, *h*, *e*, blank, *e*, for instance. Then he tried the blank for *r*, see, to make *there*. If that worked he'd gained another letter. And so on—ad bloody infinitum, I'd have said, but Perce had all the patience in the world."

He finished his tea and lit a cigarette.

"Then, one day, these people he was being so nosy about went and changed their code. Poor old Perce. I've never seen him so near being angry. He *wasn't* angry, mind you; said it wasn't scientific to be angry." Stan grinned.

"But, damn me, if he didn't get down to it all over again. It became like—like a sort of mania, I think; he *had* to go on with it. He'd got DJ121 on the brain.

"Well, then, I didn't see him much for about a fortnight before he was due to go on holiday. Then I dropped in one evening—just over a week ago now—and found him sweating away at his old code same as ever. Only this time he wasn't doing the trial-and-error business any more. No, sir. He'd broken it down completely, and he was simply decoding from a long list he'd made of the groups. And excited! Well, I wouldn't have thought old Perce could get so excited.

"By this time, I can tell you, I was a bit curious and no mistake. So I picked up one of the messages he'd just written out in plain language and started to read it. I was ready for old Perce to fly off the handle, too. Like I told you, he's cagey.

"But he didn't. He just grinned and went on with his work."

"You read the message?"

"Half a dozen of them."

"What did they say?"

"That's the hell of it. There was I expecting all sorts of gory details about white-slaving or dope-running or what have you. And what do I get? The usual claptrap. 'Olga and Mary will be arriving at eleven-thirty tomorrow. They will bring their luggage with them.' Olga and Mary!" Stan snorted.

"In fact," said Kevin, "there was a plain-language code inside the cipher."

"Correct. Or so I'd have said."

"And yet Williamson was still excited."

"I'll say he was."

"And what did you make of that?"

"Well!" Stan gestured. "There's only one thing I *could* make of it, seemed to me . . ."

"That he'd got some sort of clue to the plain-language code as well?"

"Yes. That's about the size of it."

They stared at each other in silence, each seeing the possibilities of this conclusion.

"A couple of days later," Stan concluded, "he went off on his holiday."

"He told you he was going to Ireland?"

"No, but it didn't surprise me when you said you'd seen him there. Hey—" He leaned forward. "Is he really dead?"

"As far as I know. Yes."

"Strewth!" said Stan. "Then whatever he got hold of in those messages must've been pretty hot stuff."

Kevin nodded. He wondered exactly how much "old

Perce" had really discovered about Stephen Lawlor—and in what connection. It seemed that the more they learned about the matter, the more impenetrable grew the darkness surrounding it. But he was conscious now of a vague shape in that darkness—not the small, scurrying shape of a few men intent on minor misdeeds, but something huge, ungainly and monstrously ugly. And this, he recalled, was something he had sensed from the very beginning. Now it rose up again and gripped him with the cold hands of fear.

"Listen," he said, "I told you someone had tried to kill me."

Stan nodded.

"I think it was because I know something; I discovered something by mistake—I'm not sure what. You know something, too—what you've just told us. So does Miss Dillon here. So did Percy Williamson, but they succeeded in killing him."

Stan stared for a moment in silence. Then he said, "Strewth!" again.

"You see what I mean?"

"Yes, I do."

"We're all in this together. If we stick together we stand a good chance of coming out of it—alive—together."

"Yes, but look here," said Stan, "why don't we take it all—what you know, and what I know—to the police? I reckon it's no joke."

Kevin leaned on the table, pressing his fists against his temples. "We will go to the police," he said, "soon. We've got to know something more, something definite."

"We know a lot," Stan insisted.

"No. We *guess* a lot. It's a different matter."

152

After all, he was thinking, in point of fact they knew nothing. To the police the whole thing would seem fantastic, laughable. A photographer called John Kevin, on a job in Dublin, had identified a body as a friend of his; the body had an unmistakable birthmark on its back. He had then come face to face with the friend he had just identified as dead; and this friend had admitted to having found an entirely unknown corpse lying in his flat, had admitted to having faked it up as his own body because he suspected that the man had been killed in mistake for himself, and because he didn't want whoever had done the deed to know that he was still alive. Meantime a post office engineer in Wolverhampton had disappeared because, it was said, he had discovered a secret code and had gone off like an idiot to investigate it . . .

No, no, no. It was a madhouse. The police would be convulsed with merriment. Proof was what they wanted, and rightly, not the haphazard guesses of amateur sleuths. They must find proof that could be seen and touched— proof that could be handed up to the judge for examination in a court of law.

"No," he said again, almost fiercely. "We've got to know more before we dare go to the police. And meanwhile we're in danger, each one of us. I'm sure of it."

Stan said, "Talk about the Black Dagger and all!" But there was real concern in his voice, and Kevin knew that if he joked in the face of danger it was merely the English way, quite incomprehensible to enemies and allies alike.

He said, "Well, it may sound absurd to you, but I'm no fool, Stan, and that's how I think it is. We've got to work together."

153

"Me," said Stan gesturing toward the door, "I work at Morton's. And unless I get back to the bench I'll cop it."

"But you'll help us?"

"Yes, if I can. You're the boss."

"All right. First of all keep an eye open for your own safety . . ."

"You bet."

"You'll be safer in a crowd, with a few people you know and trust near you."

Stan was grave suddenly. "Hey, you take this really seriously, don't you?"

"Yes, I do. And I advise you to do the same."

"Trust me."

"And there's one thing you can do to help if you will."

"What?"

"Can you get into the Williamson house?"

"Yes, easy. I'm in and out two or three times a week. The set sort of half-belongs to me, too, so even old Ma Williamson can't stop me if I want to play with it."

"Good. Because she'll have hysterics if she sees me again."

Stan grinned. "What'll I do when I'm in?"

"Collect any messages you can find with DJ121 on them. Have a real root around; see if you can dig out anything which might tie up with this business. We've got to have visible proof, you see. If it's possible, get into his bedroom and search that. Look in his suit pockets. Break open anything that's locked."

"Strewth!" said Stan, not for the first time. "If Ma W. catches me at that she'll have me in jug in no time."

"She mustn't catch you."

"Then?"

"Bring the loot to me at the Queen's. I'll pay all expenses, of course."

"All right," said Stan, "I'll have a bash. How about tonight?"

"The sooner the better."

Stan stood up, resplendent in his tartan shirt. "Whew," he said, "it's a proper bloody lark, isn't it? Like something out of the pictures. Don't worry though. And you can expect me with the swag at about ten tonight." He turned away, then changed his mind and came back to them.

"Hey," he said. "No kidding?"

Kevin shook his head very seriously.

Stan held out his hand and they shook solemnly. Even then he lingered, looking perplexed. "Strewth," he said finally, "doesn't seem the sort of thing that'd happen to *me*, all the same. I always knew old Perce was too clever by half." After a moment, however, he grinned.

"Talking of expenses," he said, "you can get ready to bail me out—if I fall over Ma Williamson."

John Kevin lay full length on his bed at the hotel, staring at the ceiling. Celia, staring at John Kevin, lay back in an armchair. Both of them were worn out with argument and guesswork.

"But," Celia said, "Stephen wasn't—isn't a crook. I'm not saying he hasn't done things which are outside the law, but he isn't criminal." She broke off. "Oh, don't look so *blank*. Answer me."

Kevin sighed. "In a way you're right. He's not a criminal, though heaven alone knows where the dividing line

155

runs. He has no moral sense; he despises law and order. Perhaps he's more of an anarchist, I don't know. Perhaps he's just plain crazy."

Celia stood up impatiently. "But all this evidence points to him being a crook, working with other crooks. It—it doesn't make sense."

"From the beginning," Kevin admitted, "it hasn't made sense."

"There's something missing," said the girl furiously, "something we haven't an inkling of."

Kevin rolled his head and looked at her. "Why should we care?" he asked suddenly.

It took her by surprise. She paused in her prowling about the room and looked at him wonderingly. "I've thought that, too. I lay awake most of last night thinking about it. I wondered why I was here at all."

"And why are you?"

"I thought—" She hesitated. "It seemed to me that it was because—because Stephen had betrayed me. And you. People can only go so far, I think, and then—quite suddenly—they're outside the pale; they're dangerous. I mean, however little one cares about law and order, and society, and all the rest of it, there is a limit, isn't there?"

"A limit to callousness," said Kevin dreamily. "A limit to cruelty."

"Yes. Like—like the Nazis—or the Inquisition."

He smiled at her. "You've certainly been thinking."

"And then," she said, "there's pride, too. It—hurts so terribly that somebody should think so little of one. You see I—I loved Steve. I don't mean that in any shallow way; I was willing to give him everything I had."

156

"And he?"

"He," she said, turning away so that Kevin should not see her face, "he was willing to take it all—and give nothing in return. Absolutely nothing except damnable, *damnable* charm. God, how I loathe charm."

She had broken down suddenly. Great agonized sobs racked her, and she leaned against the wall for support.

Kevin was off the bed and at her side in one movement. Her agony literally burned him inside. He seized her almost roughly and held her against his chest, saying nothing.

Again Celia felt the soothing hands of his calm presence; almost on the instant some of the pain flowed out of her, and the racking sobs became easier. And to Kevin, holding her in silence, she was no longer a child at all, but a woman whom he knew he loved. It was as simple as that. In this moment of her greatest dependence, when he might more easily think her, as he always had, a child—in this moment she grew up into a woman, and he loved her. Simple, yes; but, oh, how unutterably difficult. And, once again, all because of Stephen Lawlor, who had poisoned her with his charm and his cruelty. Kevin knew instinctively that he dare not show himself to her as a man—the complement of a woman. Not until Lawlor was dead and buried; and— what might be a longer task—not until the memory and the hurt of Lawlor were dead and buried, too.

So he merely handed her his handkerchief in silence; and, when the sobs had died away and she was calm again, he said, "Powder your nose. I refuse to look at you until you've powdered your nose."

He understood her very well now. He knew that she seized on this roughness, which was perfectly natural to him, as a merciful antidote. He knew that Stephen Lawlor would have told her—with a maximum untruth—that to him she looked lovely in tears or not. And he reflected, as she closed the bathroom door behind her, that even if it did hurt, it was as well for her to learn once and for all about men like Lawlor.

Stan arrived at ten-thirty in a state of some excitement. The cause for his excitement became apparent as he spread over the table—and later over the bed and floor—evidence of his evening's work at Number Two, The Drive, Elm Park. "Arcadia" had yielded a bumper crop.

"Strewth!" said Stan. "She nearly copped me in the bedroom all the same. I had to turn off the light quick and dive behind the door; and then, damn me if she didn't go on up to the attic to see if I was there. So I nipped in the lav quick, and pulled the chain. That stymied her."

There were, in all, forty-nine of the DJ121 messages—or scraps of messages. But it was a locked attaché case under the workbench which had produced the plums. Stan laid on the table three sheets of paper neatly tabulated.

"See," he said, laughing excitedly, "it's the keys to the codes. Must've taken old Perce months to get that lot sorted out. And look—" He pointed to the signals themselves. The first group of each, after the DJ121, corresponded to a pencilled reference at the head of each key.

Stan rubbed his hands together. He had already enjoyed his evening's larceny—in retrospect, at any rate. Some of his excitement communicated itself to Kevin and Celia.

"But that's not all," he said. "Take a look at these."

And he drew from his pocket a folded sheaf of papers

158

clipped together at the corner. The first which he laid on the table was a signal in code. Pinned to it was Percy Williamson's plain-language version. They all bent over it eagerly. It read:

To Lucy. From Victor. DJ121. Watch Manston 25th. Z/51.

Kevin said, "But . . ."

"Wait till you see this." Stan cut him short, and laid a small press clipping on the table. It was from a Birmingham evening paper dated April 26. It read:

### ROWDY MEETING
#### Police Called In

Police were summoned to a meeting of the United Freedom Movement . . .

Kevin swore under his breath.

. . . at their premises in Heber Street last night, following interruptions which led to a fight. The speaker, Mr. Tom Manston, well-known as an early champion of Socialism in Birmingham, was severely injured. He and six others, five men and one woman, are detained in hospital. A spokesman of the movement, a nonpolitical association, said that the intrusion was undoubtedly organized. There were, he said, discontented elements in their midst.

"You see," crowed Stan, "they hadn't a code word for Manston, and old Perce must've cottoned onto it at once when he saw that bit in the papers."

They stared at each other, the three of them, seeing in each other's eyes further, deeper pits of speculation.

"Now," said Stan, and he put before them another coded signal with a plain-language version attached:

To Vera. From Victor. DJ121. My Z/51 for action by you 3rd.

Celia said, "Z/51—what does it mean?"

Stan tapped the previous message with his finger. "That's what it means: 'Watch out, Vera'—Vera's a code name, of course—'Manston is at your place on the 3rd. Deal with him.'"

Kevin took the next press cutting from his hand and put it on the table. It was dated May 4. It read:

### Riotous Meeting In Liverpool
#### Freedom with Force!

Seven men and three women received minor injuries when roughs broke into a meeting of the United Freedom Movement in Dock Road, Liverpool. The speaker, Mr. Tom Manston of Birmingham, was also injured. He is reported as having said, "Some people don't agree with my interpretation of the word 'Freedom.' This is their way of trying to prevent me speaking on the subject. It isn't the first time it has happened."

"You see," said Stan. "*Vera* means Liverpool, or some bloke in Liverpool. *Lucy*'s the same for Brum."

Kevin said, "Any more about Manston?"

Stan looked at him sharply. "You don't miss much, do you, skipper? Yes, there's one more."

Heavy of heart, Kevin took the last of the sheaf. The decoded signal ran,

To Mary. From Victor. DJ121. My Z/51 to Lucy. Finalize. Z/69.

The press cutting was from a Birmingham paper; it read, as Kevin had known it would read:

### TOM MANSTON DEAD
#### Tragic Accident

The Birmingham pioneer of Socialism, Tom Manston, one-time pit boy and Trade Union leader, was drowned in Glasgow last night while on his way home from a meeting at which he had been speaker. His body was found in the now disused Caledonian Basin; it is thought that he may have slipped while crossing a footbridge and fallen under the railing. A similiar accident occurred at this same place to a nine-year-old boy last year. Although Mr. Tom Manston has recently been the center of dissension in the United Freedom Movement, of which he was a founder member, it is not thought that foul play was responsible for his death. Mr. Manston could not swim, it was stated, and in the dark it would be impossible for a stranger to find the steps which lead up the steep sides of the dock.

There was silence for a long time, the three of them lost in their own thoughts. Celia turned away and sat on the arm of the chair.

Kevin said finally, "Any more of these, Stan?"

"No. Nothing as complete as that, anyway." He produced another sheaf of paper from his pocket. "Just odd bits with question marks pencilled on them. I think that was the only one old Perce was dead sure about."

Kevin nodded. "Know anything about this United Freedom Movement?"

"Bloke at work went once or twice. All hot air, he said. He gave it up as a bad job."

"It's a cover for some sort of crookedness, no doubt about that. This Manston fellow found out too much—or knew too much and wouldn't keep quiet." He flicked over the messages. "Yes, it seems clear that *Lucy* is here in Birmingham, *Vera* means Liverpool, *Mary* means Glasgow. Who's *Victor?*"

Stan, eyes very bright, pulled yet another sheaf of papers from his pocket.

"*Victor*," he said solemnly, "is Dublin."

There was a breathless silence.

"Are you sure?"

"Perce was. Look." He laid on the table a cheap exercise book. It was Percy Williamson's wireless log. In it he kept a detailed account of the strength and clarity of the various short-wave stations he had worked with. Latterly—needless to say—the log referred to only the DJ121 stations.

Against three days in July—the 16th, 18th and 19th—he had pencilled the comment, "No transmission," and added a question mark. Later, in red ink he had starred these three dates; moreover, in the same red ink and doubtless at the same time, he had crossed out the question marks. And the reason for this was explained by another press cutting which he had folded up and fixed to the page with a paper-clip. It was brief and to the point; it read:

### POWER FAILURE IN DUBLIN

Owing to the severe strain imposed on power stations in the Dublin area of Ireland—and largely because of increased

162

industrial demands—there were breakdowns in the city's electricity supply on three occasions last week. On Monday, the damage was stated to have been repaired satisfactorily; but on Wednesday, and again on Thursday, there was a total stoppage of power. It is believed that electricity will now be rationed until a new plant, under construction, is ready for use.

Against the printed words *Monday*, *Wednesday* and *Thursday*, Percy Williamson had written the dates in red ink: *16th*, *18th*, *19th July*.

"Yes," said Kevin thoughtfully. "That looks pretty conclusive, doesn't it? Some detective, your Percy."

Stan nodded. "Patient, he was, old Perce. And I wondered what he wanted with all them newspapers. The whole place was littered with them."

The picture was very clear in all their minds—the half-tragic, half-humorous picture of Percy Williamson, eyes glinting with excitement behind the weird spectacles, crouched over his messages, brain buzzing with Morse and with the secrets of his codes. Brain, one could almost say, besotted with the task he had set himself—with the hunt which led, inevitably, to his own lonely death.

Stan broke the long silence. He said, "Well, we can't stop here. What's the orders now, skipper?"

Kevin shrugged. "Thanks for what you've done, Stan. It's a big step forward. You'll want to be going to bed."

"Bed!" replied Stan with contempt. "Me! With all these lying around?" He pointed at the signals which littered the room. "Not on your life."

His enthusiasm roused Kevin from the weariness that lay so crushingly upon him. He turned to Celia.

"No," she said before he could speak. "I won't be sent to bed either. I'd rather stay awake and work than lie awake and think."

She picked up the telephone and said, "Room Service, please. This is 491. May we have coffee and sandwiches for three, please?"

"For six," corrected Kevin, smiling.

"Make it for six," said Celia.

And so they worked, sitting around the table like industrious children with their homework. The minutes crept by and lengthened into hours. The meaningless groups of ill-assorted letters fell into place, becoming words, becoming sentences. Some were meaningless, some were pointless, some refused to emerge as sense; all were touched with a faint, underlying menace which was not lost on any of the three who laboured over them. Occasionally one or other would reach for a sandwich or a cup of nearly cold coffee. Towards one A.M. Kevin produced a bottle of Scotch from his suitcase.

The hotel noises had long since died into silence; the last drunk had long since reeled home to bed, or to the gutter. There were only the sounds of deep night now—a distant shunting of goods wagons, a sudden squawling of cats, the measured tread of a policeman patrolling empty, echoing streets.

By the time they had finished there were indications of the late summer dawn creeping up the sky—a damp dawn trailing untidy streamers of cloud. From the table the decoded messages stared up at them almost as blankly as had their coded counterparts. The address names—Lucy,

Nita, Mary, Alma, Ruth, Olga, and many others—were wildly irritating in their prim secrecy. Like expressionless ladies of the chorus they pranced across the scattered pages, dumb and improbable.

Celia, Kevin and Stan stared at each other morosely. They felt flat and enervated. The groups of haphazard letters had held some sort of promise; the plain language which decoding revealed held none.

Kevin kept picking them up, reading them, casting them aside. All, all were discreet to the point of idiocy. The emergency which had necessitated the use of Manston's name uncoded had not been repeated, and doubtless some operator had been soundly reprimanded for his lack of security. It seemed that "old Perce" had, in the case of Manston, caught the only loophole, the only chink in an armour of secrecy.

"Nothing," said Kevin furiously. "Abso-bloody-lutely nothing."

"Ditto," said Stan.

Celia held up a scrap of paper wearily between finger and thumb. "There's just one odd thing about this—"

Kevin took it from her and read, "To Vera and Alma . . ."

"Who's Vera?" he asked, frowning.

"Liverpool," said Stan.

"And Alma?"

"We don't know."

"To Vera and Alma. From Victor. DJ121. Consolidate A Sept. 14th as arranged." He glanced up at Celia. "What's so odd about this? Seems like all the rest to me— damn meaningless."

"Nothing much," she admitted yawning, "except to-day's September the 14th."

Stan said, "It might mean anything."

Celia said, "I'm not pretending it mightn't; I'm sick of the sight of the things myself. What's more, I'm going to bed." She got up and trailed away to the door. "I feel as though I'd been to a *bad* party. Good night, John. Good night, Stan."

The door closed behind her.

A few minutes later the room was dark and silent. Stan snored gently, curled up in the armchair with an eider-down. Kevin lay in bed, staring at the first sickly radiance of dawn. Presently he too fell into a deep, dead slumber.

On the table the messages stirred in a faint breath of air, and rustled as if they were alive. Disregarded now, after their moment of notoriety, they yet held the destiny of many, many people in their featherweights. And the clock ticking its way into a new day would soon—very soon now —make cruel sense of them all.

# III

KEVIN AWOKE SUDDENLY at midday. He was surprised to find that he had slept soundly for eight hours—the first real sleep he had experienced since his arrival in Dublin; and how many aeons of time ago was that? He was shocked to find that the answer was four days. He could not remember any four days of his life more crowded with incident.

The room was still in semidarkness, and he became aware presently of a shape in the armchair. Of course. Stan. Kevin sat up and switched on the bedside lamp. But it was not Stan in the chair; it was Celia, fully dressed, staring at him pensively.

"Well!" he said. "An early bird, and no mistake." He felt cheerful after his night's rest. He remembered that first meeting—*could* it be only four days ago?—in his hotel room in Dublin.

Celia said, "I slept well, too." She stood up and drew back the curtains. Then she leaned, frowning, on the windowsill.

Kevin said, "Oi! What's biting you?"

She turned, stared at him, and then continued her scrutiny of the street below.

"I've been thinking," she said finally.

"What about?"

"Those." She gestured towards the table, where last night's messages lay scattered.

"And?"

"And—" She pulled back the blind cord and let it drop against the window so that the wooden acorn on the end of it tapped irritatingly on the pane. "And— I don't know."

Kevin got out of bed and put on his dressing gown. "My dear girl!" he said.

"Yes, I know. I'm in a state, John." She looked at him over her shoulder. "I've got a whatnot."

"A what?" enquired Kevin, wondering how often these moods occurred, and how it would affect their life together—for he had quite made up his mind about that.

"A . . . Oh, what d'you call it? The thing men always laugh at us for."

"An intuition."

"Yes."

"About the messages?"

"About that one in particular—the one with the date on it. Today's date."

"And," asked Kevin—not, it's true, paying much attention to her—"whither does your intuition lead you?"

"To *Vera*," she replied, still banging about with the blind cord.

"To—?"

"Don't be thick, John. Vera—Liverpool."

168

"You mean you want to go there?"

"Yes, I do." She turned from the window suddenly and came across the room towards him. "Yes, I want to go there. Can we? Oh, do let's go there. After all, it is the obvious follow-up."

Kevin looked at the message again. "To Vera," it read, "and Alma. From Victor. DJ121. Consolidate A Sept. 14th as arranged."

"But, heavens above," he said, "it may mean no more than—than the breaking-up of some meeting, as in that Manston business."

"No, it doesn't."

"How can you tell it doesn't?"

"I—*feel* it." She looked so stricken, standing before him with a fist pressed against her chest to show where the feeling gripped her, that he had to smile.

"No, no. Don't laugh at me, John. I really do mean this. I *know* we must go to Liverpool. It's—it's a horrible feeling, too; I wish I didn't have it."

He went into the bathroom and frowned at his unshaven face in the mirror—frowned not only at the face but at the urgency in her voice, also.

"D'you remember," she went on, following him, "when you were at school, and someone came and told you the Head wanted to see you in his study at six o'clock that evening?"

"Yes, indeed."

"And it was in the middle of the morning when you were told?"

"Yes."

169

"And how you wondered whether the day would ever pass?"

"I do."

"That's how I feel now—only more so. And I hate it."

He stared at her then, where she leaned against the bathroom door, dark eyes very solemn, hair very fair with the light behind it.

Damnation take the girl, he thought. I'd go to Timbuctoo with her if she wanted me to.

"All right," he said. "Liverpool it is."

She smiled: a brief, warm smile which pierced him through and through.

After a time, still leaning there while he shaved, she said, "John?"

"Mm?"

"Do you really think Steve is in this?"

"I do. Don't you?"

"But that business about the man who was killed; the one who fell in the dock in Glasgow."

"Manston. What about him?"

"I mean if it wasn't an accident then it points to all sorts of—of thuggery. I can't connect that with Steve at all."

"Can't you?" said Kevin. "Perhaps if I tell you he was once a member of the British League of Fascists it'll help."

"*Steve* was?"

"Well, I found the badge in his stud box."

After a while she said with an effort, "Yes, I can see that; it makes sense. Callousness, and—and cruelty." She turned away into the bedroom, out of his sight, and she was silent for a long time. Then she said, "Two men couldn't be more different, could they? Than you and Steve, I mean."

170

"I don't suppose that's meant to be complimentary, but I take it as such." He followed her, wiping his face on a towel. She regarded him gravely from the window. Tousled and fresh from the washbasin he looked, she thought, very young and clean and delightful.

"Yes," she said finally. "It was meant as a compliment. I think you're about the nicest person I've ever met."

And then, while he was still breathless, she added, "You don't think by any chance Steve's up to the same Fascist larks now, do you?"

Kevin said, "I wish I could be sure he wasn't."

Celia said, "Um. I see."

Before they reached Liverpool, however, he was not at all certain to what extent men ought really to pander to the intuitions of women. Celia had hurried him through the meal which had served for both breakfast and lunch; the result was an indigestible one. And then, although there had been many things to see to—a telegram to keep Stan informed of their movements, a further visit to the car-hire firm, hotel bills to be paid—although these all required attention, she had buzzed at his elbow like an impatient mosquito. Each time he looked at her he could see in her eyes an intense, urgent preoccupation which would have been absurd were it not so alarming. Indeed, he began to catch some of her sense of prognostication—and that also he found irritating. To cap it all, they had not been ten minutes on their journey when the grey sky opened up in a deluge of rain.

Yet, as he drove—much faster than he liked—he could not help being aware of her strained, set face beside him.

171

She stared ahead at the road, only breaking her mood when he spoke; and even then her replies, though she tried manfully to make them casual, even lighthearted, were abrupt and false.

Finally he said, "Celia, do relax. You're working up for an awful attack of anticlimax."

"Maybe." She contrived a smile, and lay back in her seat. After a moment she said, "It's no good. One can't ignore feelings like this. I . . . Oh, I can't explain. Forget I'm here."

Kevin snorted. Then he said, more gently, "Just what do you expect?"

"I don't know. Something. I can't get over that message; it—it was ugly somehow. 'Consolidate.' Ugh!"

"I'll tell you what you'll find," he said. "A great grey city in the rain. Hurrying people. A few gulls. A poop or two from ships in the Mersey."

She glanced at him sharply. "Are you pretending you think that message means nothing? After what happened to Manston? After what happened to that wretched boy, 'our Perce'? After what happened to you under the railway bridge in Dublin?"

He was quite alarmed by her passion, and said nothing. After a pause she added, more quickly, "After what happened to me?"

"No," he said. "I think the message means something all right. I think they all do. Something pretty horrid, too. All I'm saying is that it'll probably be nothing more than a meeting broken up—or a couple of men coming together in a bar, and one handing something to the other under the table."

172

"Or," she said bitterly, "a man who believes in freedom being knocked on the head and pushed into a dock to drown."

The bitterness surprised him; it was an emotion he felt himself in this matter, but he had not suspected it in her.

As if sensing his thought she said, "Yes. I'm beginning to *loathe* Stephen Lawlor. And yet— And yet when I think of him—of his hair, I mean, or his eyes—of him as a man, I feel— I feel weak with a sort of sense of loss." She laughed wanly. "Mad, isn't it?"

Kevin shook his head gravely. "No. No, it's not mad. He's a very attractive person, no doubt about that."

"I think," she said evenly, "he must be crazy."

The evenness of her tone, in this particular context, pleased him all the way to Liverpool.

By hook and crook, by dint of Kevin's long experience of hotels, by exercise of Celia's dark compelling eyes and a winsome smile, they managed to get two rooms on different floors of the Adelphi. But even then—even after a soothing bath—she would not let him spend the pleasant interval before dinner lying on his bed with a dry Martini. She appeared with the evening papers, the local morning ones also, and set him to work on their damnably repetitive columns. He waded drearily through reports of damp garden fêtes, nautical weddings, flower shows and various resumés of the morning's news. The full absurdity of the search, however, lay in the fact that he did not know what he was looking for.

And after dinner—a meal which was ruined for Kevin by her nervousness and her consequent inability to eat—she could not sit still, but insisted that they should go out. She dragged him into various bars, so that they might listen to other people's conversation. She took him to Dock Road so that they might gaze at the dripping, blank façade of Number Nine where the United Freedom Movement had its headquarters, and to which—earlier in the year—police had been summoned to keep order at Mr. Tom Manston's unruly meeting.

She dragged him, protesting, up to the Cathedral and through the depressing wastes of bomb-damaged slums down to the docks. There, in more public houses, including several highly unsuitable ones which he remembered from his days as a sailor in the Liverpool Escort Force, she forced him to eavesdrop yet more blatantly, even to ask absurd and asinine questions across the bar.

And Kevin, driven, not by her promptings so much as by the intent tautness of her face, suffered all these banes, uncomplaining.

Until at last, exhausted and dripping, they stood once more in his room at the hotel.

Not looking at him, she said, "I—I'm sorry."

He could sense that it was pure physical weariness, rather than any lessening of her intuitive fears, which brought about this sudden stillness.

"That's all right. You had to do it, I know that."

"Yes, but *you* didn't." She smiled a trifle unsteadily. "Bless you."

"No. And believe me," Kevin replied with spirit, "I wouldn't have walked a step if—" he took a breath—"if you weren't you."

It hadn't been quite what he had intended to say, but it struck home all right. She nodded, withdrawn, somehow

174

lonely standing there in her wet mackintosh. All she said was, "Thank you." And then she shuddered.

"Now what?"

"I was just thinking that—that whatever it was must have happened by now. Someone may be dead, or—" Her voice trembled. "Oh, it doesn't make *sense*."

He took her by the shoulders. "You're tired. And no wonder. I'll see you to your room."

And then, as they turned, as he put out his hand to open the door, one arm about her shoulders, it happened. There was a blinding flash like monstrous lightning; it blazed across the patch of sky framed in red hotel curtains. And then, crazily, the curtains themselves leapt to life and flared out into the room; and, borne on their movement, came the explosion. Glass shattered somewhere. A woman screamed. Footsteps ran urgently down the corridor and a door banged. A woman called out, "My hat, Harry, what was that?" And even the ridiculous words could not entirely hide her fear.

In a small strangled voice, staring wide-eyed, Celia said, " 'Consolidate.' Oh, John!"

And a second later they were in the corridor, running.

The eastern sky was chaotic as Kevin swung the car out into Ranelagh Place. A hellish, flickering glare lit the undersides of billowing, struggling clouds of smoke. Celia, in that same breathless voice, said, "Follow the fire engines."

The night was panic-stricken with the clangour of bells —bells advancing to an ear-splitting crescendo; bells fading away into far distance. Little knots of people were gather-

ing on corners, and some were running towards that agonized inferno in the sky, waving their arms, shouting.

Because they had (and how absurd it seemed!) been
expecting something to happen Celia and Kevin were in the
forefront of the rush that followed. They arrived at the
yawning edge of the furnace long before any but local
sightseers, and long before official arrangements had been
made to keep people back. At once they were swept into
action, almost in spite of themselves. They had barely
time to take in the mean streets harshly lit by shifting flame,
the coiling, writhing snakes of the hoses, the stench, the
fierce waves of heat, the blank, horror-stricken faces of the
onlookers—hardly time to breathe even before a fireman
was yelling, "Give us a hand, mate. No, not you, miss."

And the two of them, for Celia naturally ignored him,
were lugging a crazy, obstinate weight of hose towards the
inferno.

"What is it?" shouted Kevin.

"Oil," roared the fireman. "About a million gallons of
it." And suddenly he was pushing them back, his face
frenzied in the shifting glare. "Get back. Run. Get
down. *Get down.*"

Kevin seized Celia's scampering figure in what might almost have been called a Rugger tackle and dragged her to
the ground behind a water-trough placed for their con-
venience by some horse-loving, Victorian philanthropist.
At the same moment the whole night sky went up in a
tremendous, awe-inspiring sheet of flame. The fierce breath
of it singed their hair as they fell, and water from the
trough poured over their backs.

Celia, unconsciously echoing Stan, said, "Strewth!"

"Strewth's right," said Kevin. "Now you damn well stay here."

They raised their heads over the trough, and were confronted by sheer horror. The fireman whom they had helped lay crumpled in an ungainly heap over his half-rolled hose. Another was dragging himself slowly towards them. Somewhere beyond—perhaps in the midst of the inferno—a man was screaming. The magnificent, revolting flames leapt roaring into what was no longer a sky, but a nightmare. The screaming man was suddenly quiet.

Out of this bedlam there emerged the solid and reassuring shape of a policeman.

"Now, you two," he said. "We appreciate the help, but this is no place for us amateurs. You get back there, right out of it, eh?"

"But—" said Celia, pointing towards the fireman. Kevin saw, with a pang, that tears were running down her cheeks —little rivulets across the grime. "But—"

The policeman grimaced at Kevin over her head. "He'll be all right," he said grimly. "We'll look after him." And he shepherded them, gravely and courteously, back towards the row of blank-faced, appalled onlookers, as though he were officiating at a royal occasion.

The fire had now spread from what appeared to be office buildings and warehouses, over a high black wall, to the end of the row of small houses.

Celia said, "I—shouldn't have cried; it made the poor policeman so embarrassed." They stood side by side watching. Tiny black figures ran gesticulating in the face of the flames or grouped themselves about hoses that squirted unavailingly into the furnace. Every minute fire engine after fire engine poured into the area, bells clanging, men shouting.

Presently in a small voice, Celia said, "The fireman was dead, wasn't he?"

Kevin nodded grimly.

They became aware of the people among whom they stood: shabby people—some in night attire, some clutching clothes, or a box, or a cage with a canary in it. They were all staring, not at the giant flames which roared into the sky out of the oil tanks, but at the small tongues of fire which leapt and danced about the houses at the end of the street. *Their* houses. Homes.

A woman said, "Just like the blinkin' war over again." She held a frightened puppy in her arms.

And a man—a middle-aged man with a mackintosh over his underwear—said, "It's them bloody Commies; you see if it ain't. Them bloody Commie bastards."

"Henry!" said his wife.

"I'd like to wring their bloody necks," he went on. "Every one of them, yes, I would. You see. It's them what done it. You see. Communists! Pah!" And he spat towards the fire.

Kevin turned, abruptly, comprehension plunging into him like cold steel—like a knife through his vitals. He found Celia's eyes already on him, and in them he saw the same horror, the same comprehension.

"Commies," said the man again. "It's them done it; you see if it ain't. Ought to be shot, the whole bloody lot of 'em."

Celia and Kevin stared at each other, eyes wide, shocked into understanding, and appalled by what they understood.

178

*part four:* **THE MEANING OF THE DREAM**

**I**F THE PAST FIVE DAYS, ever since he had set foot in Ireland, seemed to John Kevin like a nightmare, the next twenty-four hours surpassed them in every way. Up till now he had been faced by his own indecision, his own fears and suspicions; it had been the senselessness of it all that had taunted and maddened him. Now the whole business made ghastly, almost unbelievable sense: the more he considered what had happened, the more sense it made. There were, of course, many urgent questions still unanswered, but, compared with the great and terrible things he now knew, these dwindled to insignificance.

If somebody had told him, casually, that Stephen Lawlor was a Communist, and an active one at that, he would probably have laughed at them—at first, anyway. But this cold piling-up of evidence was another matter altogether; and the truth had been staring him in the face all the time, waiting for the angry voice of a man watching his house burn down to make it plain:

"It's them bloody Commies; you see if it ain't."

The little Fascist badge lying among studs and buttons

was the most direct clue of all—and he had disregarded it. Fascism or Communism; to the kind of man who must cling to an *ism*, what matter which? Indeed, for Lawlor's purposes, they were identical. And Lawlor—with his waywardness, his charm, his love of excitement, his braggadocio, his championship of lost causes and his love of semiheroic secrecy—yes, Lawlor was the perfect devotee of the *ism*. He possessed the necessary outlook: the underlying philosophy of despair. The world, Kevin realized, had always owed Stephen Lawlor a living—in Stephen Lawlor's opinion.

And yet he could risk his life to save an unknown seaman in a rough sea; and yet he would go to such extremes to get money for slum children in Dijon, or for an international settlement in Switzerland. But that, Kevin thought, was the paradox without which mania was never quite complete. Some of the worst killers have been notoriously sentimental over children, and have asked to see their favourite flower before the noose was put around their necks.

These thoughts, jumbled with too many others, milled constantly round his brain during the crazy twenty-four hours which followed the fire. Crazy, because he no longer had merely his own fears and suspicions to cope with, but the endless, involved, maddening, labyrinthine coils of that many-headed monster called Official Procedure. Now—when he knew the agonizing truth, and was burning to act upon what he knew—he was bogged down in forms in triplicate, in proper channels, in waiting rooms, in Departments X, Y, and Z—and in a thousand, million yards of bright, new, red tape.

182

He and Celia drove straight from the fire to Number Nineteen Cedar Road, Elm Park, Wolverhampton—only pausing at the Adelphi long enough to collect their belongings and pay their bill. Cedar Road at one A.M. on a wet September morning was quieter than the grave, and Stan, when roused from his bed, was in no mood for speed. But Celia, using a technique with which Kevin was all too familiar, got him into the car with a packed bag in less than fifteen minutes, and despite the horrified protestations of Stan's mum, who, it seemed, thought her boy was being "led astray."

It was half-past one when they set off for London. All went well until they reached High Wycombe, having made record time through Warwick, Bicester and Thame. At High Wycombe there were faint wraiths of mist. Kevin, knowing the road, groaned—and he had reason to groan, for at Uxbridge the inevitable fog descended on them. It was thus not until seven o'clock that they swung round Marble Arch, down Park Lane and into the hinterland of West One.

A handful of early chauffeurs with sour expressions were polishing their glittering limousines when Kevin brought his hired car to a standstill in front of 17 Pope Mews.

"Home," he said, and yawned.

Celia yawned also. "Your home?"

"My home."

Stan woke up in the back seat and yawned, too. "Home sweet home," he echoed, yawning. "Had a smashing sleep. What I wouldn't give for a cuppa char."

They trailed wearily up to Kevin's very comfortable

183

flat, and in a surprisingly few minutes were eating a large breakfast their host had prepared.

"Bread!" said Celia in astonishment. "How did you manage fresh bread?"

"I bought it," Kevin replied, "at a snack bar in Shepherds Bush when you were both fast asleep. Also the eggs."

In the cold morning light he looked extremely weary; indeed, it had been an arduous drive quite apart from the problems which occupied his mind. Celia and Stan were suddenly ashamed of themselves.

"Sleep?" said Kevin, in answer to their protestations. "I don't think I'm likely to sleep for some days." And he sat down at the telephone to ring up the only man he knew at the Home Office—a rather junior secretary.

Stan and Celia meanwhile took out the DJ121 messages and began to sort them out into sequence.

". . . Yes," said Kevin. . . . "Well, I'm sorry, Roger. How was I to know you'd only just gone to bed? . . . But I loathe night clubs myself, you know that. . . . Yes, it's very important. Vital. . . . No, I can't even give you a hint—not on the telephone. . . . Scotland Yard? . . . But can't *you* help me; it really is important. . . . Proper channels. Yes, I see. . . . Oh, go back to sleep, damn you, you always were bloody useless."

He sat staring at the receiver, as if beginning to see in its well-known shape the kind of frustration this dawning day would bring.

Presently, leaving Stan and Celia to wash up, finish sorting out the messages, and sleep, he went to Scotland Yard. There it appeared that every officer of consequence had either not yet arrived or was engaged. The unutterable complacency of the sergeant with whom he found himself closeted—coming as it did on top of his tiring drive through the night—goaded him into losing the Kevin temper. This, of course, proved fatal. The sergeant withdrew, with magnificent aplomb, behind a barricade of forms and procedures and hurt pride. He also made it fairly clear that the Yard was not unused to lunatics who wanted to waste the time of higher personages with cock-and-bull stories about spies and what-have-you.

Kevin returned, in a black fury, to Pope Mews. His head was splitting and he confidently expected to find his aides deep in glorious slumber. In which case he planned, savagely, to wake them up.

But Celia and Stan were not asleep; they were very wide-awake, indeed, and at the first sight of their tense faces Kevin knew that yet another load of responsibility was going to be added to the burden he already carried. He stood at the door, staring at them. "Now what?" he said.

"Alma," replied Celia, and added because he looked so blank, "Remember? That 'Consolidate' message was addressed to Liverpool and one other." She pushed a newspaper towards him and he took it in silence.

"Two oil explosions," he read. "Is it sabotage? Vast fires still burning in Southampton and Liverpool."

He could not go on, but put the paper down. Celia noticed that his hand was trembling.

"Seventeen people killed," she said. "Thirty-five injured." Her face was very white.

Stan gulped and added, "That's not all either, skipper."

Kevin sat down and put his aching head in his hands. "What else?"

Celia touched his shoulders lightly. "Have a cup of coffee first? I've just made it."

"What else?" demanded Kevin furiously.

Stan said, "We've managed to crack that signal we couldn't decode last night. Remember?"

"Yes."

"There was a spare group at the beginning which must mean, 'This one's coded up backwards.'"

Kevin groaned.

"Kid's stuff," said Stan. "I know. Still, it fooled us first off, didn't it?"

"Go on."

Stan pushed the slip of paper across to him. It was dated June 1. It ran:

To Vera, Alma, Lucy, Olga, Nita, Ruth, Mary, Anna, Tina, Rita. From Victor. DJ121. Stand by consolidate ABC September 14 16 18 as arranged.

"You see," said Celia, her voice strident with nerves. "*Consolidate A* was last night, September the fourteenth. This must have been the original warning message. *B* is tomorrow. *C*, two days later."

Kevin rolled his head from side to side on his supporting hands. The horror of it, and the importance of their position, made his spine prickle. He had suddenly begun to sweat.

"Those." He pointed to the ten addresses. "How many do we know."

"Four," said Stan. "*Lucy* equals Birmingham, *Vera* equals Liverpool, *Mary* means Glasgow, *Alma* means Southampton."

"*Ten* of them!" Kevin swore fiercely. "Someone's damn well *got* to listen to us."

Someone eventually did: a cold-eyed detective-inspector who gave the impression of disbelieving the story progressively, the more he heard of it. Finally—in a veritable miasma of disbelief—he gathered up the copies they had made of the important signals and said, "The constable will show you to the waiting room. I can't say just when I shall be able to get these to Sir Charles, but, of course, I shall expedite the matter."

"Expedite!" said John Kevin savagely when they had been sitting in the waiting room, watched by their constable, for an hour. "Expedite my Aunt Fanny!"

The constable coughed deprecatingly, and studied his fingernails. The clock ticked on. At lunchtime they were freed, with a request that they should return inside the hour. At half-past two the cold-eyed detective-inspector reappeared and summoned them to the office of an older but more human individual who was, it soon became clear, only a few rungs higher on the hierarchical ladder. Kevin repeated the story. Notes were taken. They returned to the waiting room.

At teatime Kevin lost his temper again. It was spectacular. Celia and Stan, sitting primly on their bench, watched while constables and sergeants succeeded each other in a dizzy and outraged procession. The cold-eyed inspector appeared briefly, was called an "incompetent ass," and withdrew swearing.

Finally, in a voice of thunder, Kevin told the world at large, "I'm going to the House of Commons right now." And they all swept out, and, what is more, *went* to the House of Commons.

There, after waiting for a further half-hour, they were joined by a young and very correctly dressed Member with an engaging grin; he appeared to be an old friend of Kevin's, and he listened gravely to the extraordinary story, which, as it unfolded, seemed to become more and more unbelievable. Once or twice the young Member's eyebrows shot up to dizzy heights, and he darted quick, appraising looks at one or other of them. Presumably what he saw inclined him to pay greater attention to what he heard; the three strained, weary faces were not unimpressive. His grin faded away; he became stern, then worried, then alarmed.

"Now," said Kevin in conclusion, "whether you believe us or not, you must, you *must* agree that it's got to be looked into."

The other nodded. "Yes, it has. There's an awful lot missing, by the way."

"Heavens above," cried Kevin, much too loud for those hallowed precincts, "if I told you the whole story we'd be here till midnight."

"I see." He was silent for a while. "Of course, you shouldn't have gone to the Yard at all; it'll be Patchway's job."

"Who's he?"

"Special Department. Good fellow, too. Look here,

188

this'll take time, old boy. The Home Secretary's in America, as you know; and the Undersec's at it hammer and
tongs this very minute, trying to answer a lot of very
sticky questions. It's his pigeon, though. I'll attack him as
soon as I can."

"But," said Celia, "it's *tomorrow*. And it's addressed to
ten different places."

The young Member was by now adept at catching their
allusions; he understood this one. "Yes, I can see the urgency."

"Supposing," said Celia, "*ten* oil depots go up in smoke."

Something of the horror in her voice touched them all.
The young Member looked very grave indeed. "I'll be as
quick as I can," he said. "The best thing for you to do is
to get some sleep—all of you. I know your number, John.
I'll ring you as soon as I get results."

"Sleep!" said Kevin bitterly—for the second time that
day—as they emerged from the grandiose portals of government. "Sleep!"

They stood together under the soaring Gothic façade
and thought enviously about sleep. It was now six o'clock
in the evening. The buses which swirled round Parliament
Square were crowded with homing workers.

"Sleep," said Stan, yawning. "Strewth, what I couldn't
do with a drop of that!"

But, as they all knew perfectly well, sleep was out of the
question. They were overtired and their nerves were on
edge; moreover, they were in the grip of a furious, impotent impatience. The bumbling and bungling of officialdom
had never seemed so crass, so positively criminal.

At a quarter to eight the telephone rang. It was the young Member letting them know that the Undersecretary had the matter before him now—he was in touch with Scotland Yard, with the police at Southampton and Liverpool, and with the Special Department. The young Member advised them to get some sleep; it was clear that the weariness and the agonized impatience of their faces had impressed him.

It was equally clear that the Undersecretary of State for Home Affairs and his corps of advisers, not having seen the faces in question, were not so impressed. The minutes ticked by and lengthened into hours.

Kevin, Celia and Stan began to avoid each other's eyes. They tried playing the radiogram; they tried Australian rummy; they tried patience—a singularly inappropriate game. They tried expressing their views on the muddle-headed, ham-fisted, clod-footed behaviour of Whitehall. They tried coffee; they tried bacon and eggs; they even tried to sleep.

And it was sleep, finally, which had its way with them, as, one way or another, it always will. Stan succumbed first, full-length on the floor, his head pillowed on two cushions. Kevin put an eiderdown over him, and he never stirred. For a while he and Celia sat side by side on the settee playing dominoes. And then, between two moves, her head lolled against him. He put an arm round her shoulder, and she sighed.

And presently Kevin—thus trapped into sitting still—grew drowsy, cursed officialdom roundly for a precious day wasted, fell asleep himself.

190

The clock ticked its way into September the sixteenth. And on the ticking clock, on the folded message—"Consolidate B"—in Kevin's pocket, hung the destiny of thousand upon thousand of sleeping people.

THE NIGHTMARE twenty-four hours of frustration and indecision ended at ten o'clock next morning. Officialdom awoke, yawning, and decided that this matter of Mr. John Kevin and his Communist cloak-and-dagger story might bear inspection. With reservations. There are always reservations in government offices, for the simple reason that no one wants to perform the delicate operation known as "taking the can back."

At ten o'clock the atmosphere of repressed frenzy in Kevin's flat was broken by the hysterics of the telephone bell.

An unhurried, but agreeably efficient woman's voice said, "Is that Mr. Kevin?"

"It is."

"This is S.D.3. Secretary. Colonel Patchway's office."

"Yes."

"The Colonel is sending a car for you right away. Will you be ready?"

"We are."

"Good. By the way, the car is actually a taxi; will you

treat it as such, though, of course, there's no need to pay. We use it when a degree of secrecy is necessary."

With which astonishing news, she rang off.

At last, as Stan put it, the penny seemed to have dropped. At last officialdom had opened the massive doors of its temple. Fifteen minutes later they were being ushered into a lofty, bare office overlooking Belgrave Square, and a lean, grey-haired man was rising from his desk to greet them. They were introduced to a dapper, young secretary from the Home Office called Tippett and a thick-set, middle-aged man called Farquarson, who looked like a not very successful schoolmaster, but was in fact an extremely successful detective.

Colonel Patchway himself was more the conventional idea of a barrister than a soldier; he had a long, fine face, deeply scored, weary grey eyes and a gentle, precise voice.

"Now," he said, "you must be very impatient after your long wait. I shan't apologize because it's no fault of mine. However, your—your very extraordinary story has now been passed to me—with reservations . . ." He glanced wryly at Mr. Secretary Tippett, who returned the glance with cold hauteur. "You'd better tell me the whole story; don't miss out anything."

Kevin told them. He started with the identification of what he had supposed to be Lawlor's body; he touched on Celia's first early-morning visit to the hotel; on the two attempts to take his life; on his illegal entry into Mr. Tony Grant's flat, and his meeting there with the man he had thought to be dead.

He recounted Stephen Lawlor's explanation—that involved lie about the running of drugs from Paris—and he went on to explain his first attempts at detection: the care-taker at the flat and the four "clumsy sort of fellers" who had visited Lawlor there. He told them how he had traced one man, Mr. B. Tanner of Newcastle-on-Tyne, to the squalid Alpha Hotel, and how it had suddenly occurred to him that if he could see the passport, which he knew to be in Lawlor's possession, he might discover the identity of the man who had really died.

He described how the passport had led him to the Williamson house in Wolverhampton, to the meeting with Stan and to the discovery of the messages—and how that ominous DJ121 had tied up with the note in Stephen Lawlor's diary.

Then—in a dead, intent silence—he told them of Celia's intuition, of their journey to Liverpool, of the fire, and of that chance remark which had suddenly made it all horribly plain to them.

When he stopped speaking the silence continued, pregnant with thought. Kevin took the final signal from his pocket and laid it on Colonel Patchway's desk. The three men bent over it, their faces tense and alert.

"I see," said Patchway finally. "The inference is that this is some sort of plan to take place in three parts on three alternate days."

"The *inference!*" Kevin burst out. "Isn't it more than that?"

The man called Farquarson smiled comfortably over his pipe. He spoke for the first time, a faintly Scots overtone in his voice. "Aye, it's more than that, all right. But you'll have tae get used to our way of talking. Everything's an inference till there's proof."

194

Colonel Patchway stood up and walked over to one of the tall windows overlooking the Square.

"Yes," he said after a while, "it's more than an inference, all right." His face was very grave. "Since you three young people know a good deal more about this than even the highest government official outside this room—" he grinned again at Mr. Secretary Tippett of the Home Office—"there's no point in holding back official secrets, is there?"

Mr. Tippett looked as though he might disagree with this reasoning, but Patchway went on speaking before he could remonstrate. "We've suspected for some time now that, in the event of armed aggression by the Russians in Europe, one of their first moves in this and allied countries would be a large-scale sabotage operation. Yes, you may well look shocked."

"But," said Kevin, "you can't— You don't think this . . ."

Patchway frowned. "How can one be sure? I think it's unlikely myself. The latest information from behind the Iron Curtain gives no indication that war is imminent."

"Then . . ."

"The inference—" He smiled faintly at the word this time. "The inference is that this is something in the nature of a dress rehearsal—a testing of the organization. If so— and if you have really discovered the—the arteries of the thing, as it were—then you've done an extremely valuable service to the country."

Stan said, "Strewth!"

Colonel Patchway gave his tired smile. "Yes. 'Strewth' just about sums it up. Now we, here, have a fairly comprehensive and adaptable organization. We have, of course, men in all the big industrial towns and docks. As a matter of fact, our fellow in Liverpool did get an inkling of some kind of trouble afoot there, but he could find no way to follow it up."

"But," Celia burst out, "it's a quarter to eleven now, and it's the sixteenth—and that message . . ."

Patchway waved his hand to quiet her. "My dear Miss Dillon, I know exactly how you feel; I could feel the same if I allowed myself to do so. And *if* I allowed myself to do so I should long ago have been a nervous wreck. In this department we are only given so much freedom; we work directly under the Home Office." He glanced at Mr. Tippett, who was looking offensively bored.

"But . . ." said Kevin.

"And the Home Office," Patchway concluded, "are not wholly convinced that your story is not— How shall I put it? Not *contrived*."

In the small, ugly silence which followed this shocking statement, Stan said, "Strike a bloody light!"

"Once again," replied Patchway, "you've hit the nail on the head. I echo your sentiments: 'Strike a bloody light!' " And he gave Mr. Secretary Tippett a far from friendly glare.

"My authority," said that gentleman in a high, and highly educated, voice, "wish to be *quite* sure, if you'll excuse my saying so, that your discoveries—though doubt-less well-intentioned as far as you are concerned—are not *in themselves* a clever ruse to disrupt the public services: the police mainly, of course."

"Oh, damnation!" said Kevin. "Aren't you being too clever by half?"

"It's pleasant," added Patchway, "to have unofficial spokesmen for one's every thought." And the big man, Farquarson, rumbled with mirth and said, "Hear, hear," at his most Scottish.

Mr. Tippett flushed. "We are dealing," he went on, "with an enemy—I beg your pardon—with a prospective enemy who have, in the past, used every conceivable kind of subtlety. My authority is convinced that in this case, as in others, we must take all reasonable precautions to cover ourselves from every angle against such subtlety. Moreover . . ."

"But don't you see?" Celia was on her feet suddenly, her voice far from controlled. "While you're sitting there blathering, and trying to cover yourself from every angle, people may be dying. They may be dying right now. Why, it's—it's *crazy*."

She sounded very Irish in this tirade, and it left her flushed and trembling. Kevin put up a hand and touched her arm. She sat down abruptly. Mr. Tippett was gobbling like an outraged turkey; Colonel Patchway was trying not to smirk; Farquarson was heaving with perfectly unconcealed mirth. "Good lass," he said. "Good lassie."

"I think," Patchway said, "that I can assure you, Miss Dillon, that there won't on this occasion be any deaths; broken heads maybe, but not deaths. I hope not, anyway."

"You mean," said Kevin, "that you actually *know* . . ."

"Reports from observers," Patchway began, "indicate . . ."

But at that moment there came a tap on the door. A smart young man said, "Excuse me, sir. Top priority,"

197

and handed the Colonel a slip of paper. Patchway read it, and nodded to himself.

"This—" he poked the paper under Tippett's nose—"may interest your authority." Then, turning: "My observers were right. The first one's started—here in London."

"First what?" demanded Kevin.

"Strike," replied Patchway.

In the next hour reports came in from Bristol, Cardiff, Liverpool, Glasgow and Hull. All stated that labour troubles—if not bona-fide strikes—had held up the unloading of ships. In Cardiff and Glasgow the hold-up was almost one hundred per cent.

In the hour following there were reports, more or less serious, from Newcastle, Swansea and Southampton.

Patchway, though full of suppressed fury, was cool enough on the surface. "You see," he said. "There it is. There's been nothing like it since the twenties."

Kevin was aghast. "But have these people so much influence?"

"Not exactly. But they know that once unrest is stirred up and the men set against the unions—or the unions against the employers—as long as everyone is set against everyone else, the ensuing negotiations and discussions are just a vast unwieldy machine out of control. All they have to do is to start the machine up. Of course, there's been nothing like this for years; it was thought to be impossible. Now perhaps a few people will realize that *nothing* is impossible where fanatics are concerned."

At this point, Mr. Secretary Tippett, who had been sitting by the telephone in an adjoining office for the past half-hour, returned somewhat chastened, and said, "They're talking about a state of national emergency. Martial law and heaven knows what."

"I take it then," observed Patchway dryly, "that I can now go ahead and do what I proposed doing last night—now that it's too late."

"Yes," said Mr. Tippett, and withdrew in haste.

They were all of them on their feet by this time: it was not an occasion for sitting down. And it was Celia, with that singleness of purpose which seemed to have seized her, who pointed to the message on Patchway's desk and said, "But what about C? What about the last part of the plan?"

The Colonel sat down and looked at the slip of paper lying under her finger.

"There again," he said, "we've got our feelers out. It'll probably be transport. In any case that's the next obvious step."

"The railways?"

"Yes, and the roadways. There's already been trouble in one or two goods yards—notably Euston and Crewe; and there's what they will persist in calling a token strike actually going on in the shops at Swindon."

He looked worried as he spoke, so clearly worried that Kevin said, "And?"

"And I'm afraid that if they can't work up labour trouble, they'll only resort to a bit more sabotage. It wouldn't surprise me if they didn't have a dab at the power stations. It's impossible to say what's in their minds. It *might* even be the real thing, but I don't think so. If it were, we'd have reports already of the same sort of situation in America and France—and certainly in Germany. That doesn't make it any less awful. And it doesn't alter the fact that if we can get to the roots of the organization now we can probably give them such a weeding that they won't recover at all."

"The roots?" echoed Celia wonderingly.

"Aye," said Farquarson from his corner. "The roots. And that means Dublin."

Patchway gave John Kevin a searching look. "And Dublin," he said, "means you, young fellow." His voice was very level, and very sincere now.

"Me?"

"Yes—if we can achieve anything before the eighteenth. If we're going to nip this damnable thing—if not in the bud, then before it's in full flower."

"Me?"

Patchway motioned them all to sit down.

"Listen," he said, "Ireland's a foreign country, d'you realize that?"

"Yes."

"Remember in the last war how they wouldn't retreat one inch? How the place was a breeding ground of enemy spies, and informers and God knows what other dirt?"

"Yes."

"That's called being neutral. Sorry, Miss Dillon, but some of us still feel strongly about it. If we'd been able to have a base or two on your West Coast—as in the '14-'18 affair—there's no telling how many of our sailors wouldn't have died. However, no matter. The point is that if we're to work in Ireland, *officially*, it's going to mean a lot of

200

diplomatic twaddle. It's going to mean time. You understand?"

"Yes."

"But if you go back there on holiday—and maybe if
Farquarson here goes with you—"

"I see."

"I'm glad you see, Mr. Kevin, because in my opinion
it's our only hope."

"But what do you expect me—us to do?"

"Several things. Mind you, we shall get the business
moving from the official point of view as well; you'll be,
as it were, the advance guard. Believe me, the Irish aren't
fond of Communists, and their police force is first-rate; it's
only the official angle, the diplomatic hocus-pocus, that's
going to hold us up. Farquarson here has one or two con-
tacts in the force in Dublin; you won't be entirely on your
own."

Kevin had not even heard this last part because Celia—
moved perhaps by the sense of imminent danger which
charged the atmosphere of this quiet office—had slipped
her hand into his. It took him entirely by surprise.

"Now," Patchway went on, "this is roughly what we
propose. You, Miss Dillon and Farquarson will fly to Dublin in the ordinary way. There's a plane from Northolt at
one o'clock. Naturally you'll get seats; we'll see to that.
You—" he glanced at Stan—"will stand by here in our wireless room: it will almost certainly be necessary to send out
signals to these headquarters—" he tapped the message—
"using their code, of course.

"So far so good.

"When you get to Dublin you'll have two objectives.

One, to get control of their transmitter, the originator of all these DJ121 messages."

"Victor," said Celia.

"Yes, Victor. If you can't get control, then you must put it out of action. In either case one or other of us must, by tomorrow evening at the latest, send out a signal cancelling Part C of their operation."

Stan whistled through his teeth.

Kevin said, "But how are we going to trace this transmitter? Is there time to do direction-finding, and all the rest of it?"

Patchway shook his head. "Neither time nor the facilities—not at such short notice, anyway. You'll have to do what you can with plain detection. Farquarson's pretty good on detection." He cocked an eye at Kevin. "Besides, we thought you might have ideas."

"Well—there's this United Freedom Movement. They have a place in Dublin, and it seems to be involved somehow."

"Most certainly it's involved." Patchway banged his desk. "It's just the sort of damn silly, crackpot affair which these people love to get hold of. I doubt if three-quarters of its members know what's going on. This fellow Manston did." He waved the messages and the press cuttings. "No doubt about that. He paid for the knowledge too.

"No. Detection is the only kind of direction-finding we can use. And, of course, we've got the dear old military advantage of surprise in our favour. I don't for a moment suppose that they suspect you of being half as intelligent as you've shown yourselves to be. Their general inclina-

202

tion is to underestimate everyone not of their own—should I call it faith? We've got to hope that they don't know you've come to see me, either. Hence the secrecy—the taxi we sent for you instead of a car, and the somewhat round-about route the driver took to get you here."

Kevin said, "How about this second objective in Dub-lin?"

"I'm coming to that." He stood up and walked away to the window again; it seemed a habit with him when he wished to think. "It's this fellow, Stephen Lawlor," he said at length. Kevin felt Celia's hand grow rigid in his; he squeezed it reassuringly.

"For some time," Patchway continued, "we've known about Lawlor. During and after the war this department was greatly concerned with recalcitrant servicemen and their—their indiscretions. Lawlor was one of them. He was picked up at Portsmouth once with a gas mask case full of watches and bottles of Chanel No. 5. He's been on the fringes ever since, but he keeps out of this country as much as he can. However, we have had reports from Paris and elsewhere. We suspected three years ago that he had a pinkish tinge about him; just when he went bright Red I couldn't say. The point is—" He regarded Kevin and Celia gravely. "The point is that there's now little doubt that he is Victor—virtually in charge of this operation."

There was silence in the big room. A bluebottle buzzed about the ceiling. A telephone rang in some other office.

"Part two of your mission," said Colonel Patchway, "is to get Lawlor—one way or another."

Kevin heard the swift intake of Celia's breath. He said,

203

"But he may not be in Dublin. He came to England using the false passport."

"Yes." Patchway nodded. "And he went back to Dublin next day using another one—a stolen one this time."

"Why didn't you stop him?"

"Because," said the Colonel wearily, "the theft of the passport wasn't reported until too late, and we can't go about arresting people at airports because they look like someone on our dossier. Our man thought it might be Lawlor, but the passport was quite in order. Besides, we've no evidence against him—not enough to hold him, anyway. Not yet."

"Then you can't be sure it *was* him?"

"We're pretty sure now. Of course—" He smiled his tired smile. "If you had seen your way to coming forward a day earlier we should probably have been able to arrest him—a charge of using Williamson's name and papers. However, that's neither here nor there now. The main point is that he would hardly be absent from the controls during this, to his people, extremely important operation."

"No, I suppose not." Kevin still looked doubtful all the same. "I don't quite see how we're to find him."

Patchway tapped his long fingers together pensively. "Don't you?" he said lightly.

"No."

"In that case I'd better tell you, *before* you agree to undertake this—mission."

Kevin glanced up sharply.

"They've already tried to kill you twice," Patchway explained evenly. "I think—if we make your arrival in Dublin fairly public—that there'll be no need for you to

204

go to him; it's extremely likely that *he* will come to *you*. If you get my meaning?"

"Oh," said John Kevin, swallowing with sudden difficulty. "I see."

## III

As soon as he stepped out of the plane at Dublin Airport John Kevin knew that he was back in the world of nightmare. It almost seemed that the whole infuriating business was about to begin over again: that he would presently find himself sitting on a stool in the cocktail bar of the Melbourne Hotel while the page boy's voice —the banshee wailing in some mist-haunted bog—called his name, summoned him to the manager's office, and delivered him over to the police; and they, of course, would tell him, with prevarications, that a friend of his had been killed in a car accident. The sense of repetition was overpowering —and so was the sense of fear. There was something cold-blooded and crazy about being used as bait; he knew now how the kid must feel when it was pegged out in the jungle at nightfall to entice a marauding leopard. He was, moreover, quite certain that he was being watched from the crowded terraces of the airport building, and that presently someone up there would go to a telephone, dial a number and say, "He's here; he's back."

However, he had been carefully rehearsed in the part

he must play, and he gave a reasonable performance of Act One, Scene One, in the hall of the airport. Here he said good-by to Celia, told her that he would telephone her in the evening, and watched her driven away by Finian in her uncle's car. He then climbed into the Dublin bus, ignored Farquarson, who was already installed there—looking exactly like a schoolmaster on holiday—and settled himself in the back seat.

At the City Air Terminal he wasted as much time as possible, making vacuous enquiries, in order to let Farquarson reach the Melbourne well ahead. Once alone in the midst of so many milling people, it was all he could do to prevent himself glancing fearfully over his shoulder every few seconds. Colonel Patchway's assurance that no attempt would be made on his life in public did not seem very authoritative now, and he was extremely relieved to arrive at the hotel.

It had been arranged that he and Farquarson should occupy adjoining rooms with a bathroom between. As far as the world was concerned the bathroom belonged to Kevin: the communicating door which led to the policeman's room was locked and bolted, and the two men would never be seen together in public. Once their bedroom doors were closed, however, they could meet and discuss their plans. Kevin had not been in his room more than a minute before he heard the key in the lock and Farquarson's reassuring shape emerged from the bathroom, smiling. In his hand was a sheaf of papers. He waved them at Kevin.

"The Colonel was right," he said. "We aren't going to get much co-operation—not until official representations have been made by the Foreign Office." He grimaced.

207

"Listen to this. Let me see. Oh, yes. . . . 'We are quite satisfied that the man, Lawlor, of whom you speak, is dead. His body was identified beyond all shadow of doubt by a close friend. Enquiries are now being made as to the cause of death, since it is believed that Lawlor may have been killed by associates in the smuggling of narcotics. Although he had not been resident in this country for some years, we would draw your attention to the fact that Lawlor was an Irish subject, in possession of an Irish passport.' " Farquarson folded the letter neatly. "Which means, 'Mind your own business.' The answer is that we're on our own until the F.O. gets moving, and that may not be for weeks." He sounded perfectly happy about the state of affairs. "This—" he waved the letter—"is from your old friend O'Connor, by the way."

Kevin nodded glumly. He had thought that the style seemed familiar.

"The question is," Farquarson went on, "just where are we going to start, the noo?" His sudden lapses into Scots phraseology struck Kevin as being affected and irritating. He did not reply in consequence. Farquarson, settling into the room's only comfortable chair, eyed him blandly. "I think," he said, "you'd better put in an appearance at this United Freedom Movement."

"Not alone," replied Kevin with firmness, remembering how the old vulture had scowled up at him from the basement of 144 Antrim Street.

"I was thinking," said Farquarson, picking his teeth, "that you could take along the Irishman you told us about. Miss Dillon's uncle's fellow."

"Yes, I could."

208

Farquarson, lumped into the armchair, looked so untidy, so mild and so utterly harmless that Kevin's sense of insecurity returned, intensified a hundredfold. He had not, of course, heard any of the stories which circulated in the underworld about the man who sat facing him; if he had, he would have known that the untidiness and the lumpishness and the general air of amateur incompetence were a mask. What lay beneath was much respected in the underworld, and there was justification for some of the uglier legends attached to him, too. He could be quite ruthless.

"By the way," said Kevin, "we don't know if there's a United Freedom meeting tonight."

"Yes, we do. 'The Free Individual and the Free Community', by Harold Schleiffer. At seven o'clock. Discussion and refreshments to follow."

There was, Kevin realized suddenly, more to Farquarson than met the eye.

"What'll I do when I'm in?" he asked.

"Keep your eyes and ears open. We've got to find a lead of sorts. Maybe it'll be this chap." He waved an enlarged print of the photograph which Kevin had taken in the Melbourne foyer; the narrow rat face was most unwholesome in close-up. "Or you may see somebody called away urgently. Someone we can follow. Or—" He smiled. "Or your Mr. Stephen Lawlor may make his third attempt."

Kevin looked startled.

"Don't worry," said Farquarson. "I shan't be far away."

This, because he had as yet no opinion at all of the policeman's capabilities, was scant reassurance to Kevin.

"How d'you mean 'shan't be far away'?"

209

Farquarson heaved with mirth. "We may not be getting *official* co-operation, but I've a few old friends in the guard, remember. And it's not hard to get an Irishman interested in a scrap."

"You think there'll be a scrap," said Kevin.

"I do. The United Freedom people have a long, long history of trouble behind them."

Farquarson took from his pocket a most serviceable-looking revolver, and held it out. "Don't use it unless you have to," he said. "And *if* you have to, don't hesitate."

The basement of 144 Antrim Street was painted pale green and lit by six dangling electric-light bulbs with harsh white shades. The room must once have been a vast kitchen populated by head cooks and tweenies. Now, in the scene of their captivity, the United Freedom Movement juggled with the polemics of something no tweeny had dared to think of. It was, Kevin thought wryly, all very absurd.

On the green walls were pinned posters of the Granite-Hewn-Worker and Sunrise-of-Liberty variety. At one end of the room was a platform: chairs, and a table with a carafe of water on it. Behind the platform hung a large blue banner, a tangle of doves and olive leaves at its centre. Untidy lines of hard chairs filled the remaining space. This Temple of Freedom was reached through an anteroom. painted the same glacial green, in which was a trestle table covered with cups and saucers and plates of buns. An ancient tea urn hissed in the corner. The atmosphere was intensely depressing.

As soon as Kevin and Finian entered the anteroom they

came face to face with the mad vulture of Merrion Square, who was, it soon became evident, local secretary of the Movement. He was talking to a massive woman with bangs touching her eyebrows; as the evening wore on the bangs became more and more wild until at last she resembled nothing more nor less than an old English sheepdog. The vulture gave Kevin a startled look of very evident distress, but managed to continue his conversation with the sheepdog.

Satisfied with this reception, and with the faunal simile, Kevin glanced about the room and found many other feathered or furred types. There was a young man exactly like a timid white rabbit, and another with all the ponderous, glowering attributes of an irritated bear. There were various parrotlike women and one, in a dirty mackintosh, who resembled a seal so closely that the effect was startling.

Altogether there were some twenty-five people in attendance—some chattering in the anteroom, others already filing into the kitchen to take their seats.

Finian—thereby disclosing his real interest in the proceeding—said, "I'll be damned if it looks like a fight to me. The divil take me if any one of them could raise a little finger to a mouse." He looked aggrieved, a dark scowl creasing his saturnine face.

At this moment the first astonishing thing of the evening occurred. The old vulture suddenly appeared, plucking, at Kevin's elbow. He drew them aside conspiratorially and hissed, "They've gone, sir. Now you must believe me; there's never a one of 'em here now. We don't want any

211

trouble, and I must make that clear. D'you understand now? We don't—want—any—trouble."

Kevin stared.

"I'm not saying I believe everything I hear about your friend, Mr. Lawlor; I thought him a fine man and I'm not inclined to change my beliefs easily. But—" he tapped Kevin's chest with a long, yellow finger—"we—are—*not* a political organization. Russia may have the answer, I'll not argue about that. We can agree to differ now, can't we?" He grinned fearsomely, and Kevin realized with amazement that the man was afraid—that it had been fear which had sent him scampering down the area steps at their last meeting.

"But . . ." he began.

"No trouble," squawked the other. "Your people have caused a lot of trouble here—and in England, too. We keep our meetings friendly. Russia may be right, I grant you, but—we—are *not* a political organization."

It was perfectly clear to Kevin what lay behind this complex recital. He remembered how he had told the vulture that Lawlor was his friend; the strange creature had taken this information to its logical conclusion. Knowing what he now knew about the United Freedom Movement, Kevin could make sense of so much which had once been meaningless. What perfect dupes—what a perfect cover for Communist activity—these people were, with their windy theses and their prating about liberty.

"And so," said the vulture, almost wheedling now, "you'll go, won't you? There's nothing here. We haven't seen your people for weeks."

But his pathetic fear and his earnestness were no match

for what he was up against. He had hardly stopped speaking when the door opened and two new arrivals came into the room. Kevin felt his heart give a jerky leap; he put a hand into his coat pocket and touched the cold, reassuring shape of the revolver which Farquarson had given him. For there was no mistaking the new arrivals, with their stupid, childishly casual expressions—with their way of entering a room sideways, back towards the nearest wall, little eyes flickering over the assembled people. They were of the genus Thug.

Finian nudged Kevin, his eyes alight suddenly. "That's more like it," he said.

Kevin was no Irishman; he was no coward, either. But he did not like fights. His heart, after its initial leap, sank into his stomach and lay there palpitating nervously. He cursed Patchway, secure in his office, and Farquarson, heaven knew where—*and* Finian, standing beside him with the light of battle in his dark eyes.

Patchway had said, "It's extremely doubtful that these people know you are in possession of so much evidence. And I'm hoping that they have no idea at all that you have reported what you've discovered to the police. This will make it more essential to them that they intercept you before you do so. And, to us, it is vital that they should try to intercept you."

"In fact," Kevin had said, "I'm the worm on the hook."

And Patchway, smiling, had said, "Exactly."

Kevin now cursed him roundly.

Hard on the heels of the first two men came a third and after him three more. Their hard, callous presence could be felt—a chill fog pervading the room. The parrot chat-

213

terers, the white rabbit, the bear and the seal fell silent suddenly, sensing the wolves amongst them. Then all together, they made for the inner room.

It was a clammy, unpleasant silence which greeted Mr. Harold Schleiffer as he rose to speak on "The Free Individual and the Free Community."

Mr. Schleiffer was evidently of American origin; he was, moreover, a man of great sincerity—patent sincerity, which shone out of his myopic eyes behind their rimless spectacles. He was flabby and fair, and he had doubtless been warned that there might be trouble. He was very nervous.

Kevin had never realized, until he heard Mr. Schleiffer speak, how dangerously near to Communism were the majority of conventional phrases about freedom. In almost every sentence, the pudgy, short-sighted man delivered some absurd tag which might have been lifted bodily from a Soviet textbook. In this way, Kevin thought, the preaching of Marx had reached out into the hearts of simple, sincere men, leaving a seed there for his inheritors to cultivate as they chose. No wonder the good Party members had found United Freedom such rich soil for the additional sowing of their own particular seed—the seed of dissension. In all but name the people listening so intently to Mr. Harold Schleiffer in this room were Communists. It was a grisly thought.

But John Kevin had other things on his mind; he could not give the speaker all his attention, since it was more concerned with six blank-looking gentlemen sitting somewhere behind him. He had led Finian to the front row of chairs, wishing at that moment to put as much space—and

214

as many people—as possible between himself and the six.
Now he regretted having done so; it was impossible to
know what they were up to back there beyond the intent
faces of the disciples of freedom. It was, moreover, impossible to converse with Finian under the quick eyes of the
vulture, who sat nervously at the edge of his chair on the
platform waiting for trouble.

Kevin took an old envelope from his pocket and, hoping that it looked as though he were taking notes, wrote,
"I think the six thugs may be out to get me. It's no good
fighting. Odds too great. How can we escape?"

Finian, when he read this, showed very clearly by his
expression that he did not think discretion the better part—
or any part at all—of valour.

Kevin took the envelope back, discreetly, and wrote,
"When I say 'get' me, I mean *kill* me. I'm not staying for
that."

This addendum seemed to bring the matter home to
Finian; he—even he—looked startled. Both of them began
to examine the room in which they sat for means of exit.
Kevin, as he did so, found time to wonder what in heaven's
name he had agreed to Farquarson's suggestion for, in the
first place. It was surely obvious that there would be no
clues here—or none that he, an untrained observer, could
discover. He was aware of a cold sweat in the small of his
back. He felt trapped. In spite of Finian, he felt alone; he
felt that Farquarson had deserted him and that, presently,
he was going to be battered to death for no reason at all.
He was furiously angry, more than afraid, because of all
the photographs yet to be taken. And there was Celia, too.
How much would he now prefer to be sitting with her

over an amiable tête-a-tête dinner at the Melbourne. Yes, he was angry. Anger grew inside him as he had known it grow so often before. The pulse in his temple began to throb; he began to tap with his shoe on the floor; he went —though he could not know it—a rich shade of pink.

Damn Farquarson, he thought. And Patchway, and Finian, and bloody Lawlor, and Dublin. And Mr. Harold Schleiffer so earnestly intent on his *isms*.

Temper is a strange, unpredictable taskmaster with an impatience which quickly mounts beyond control. Temper is no disciple of reason either—a fact which is seldom much use to those who possess quick tempers. In this case, however, it came to John Kevin's aid.

He suddenly thought, Why the hell am I sitting here on this revoltingly hard chair in this revolting room, surrounded by these revolting people, listening to a lot of adolescent poppycock?

Temper burst in a cloud of blood before his eyes. He said one rude descriptive word very loud, stood up and made for the door, with Finian in pursuit.

He could not, in cool deliberation, have made a better tactical move. The six thugs in the back row had either tipped their chairs or had their hands in their pockets or their legs twined around the chair in front of them. The only one who leapt up to bar the way received a straight right from Kevin—a complete fluke since he could not even see the man clearly—and a much neater straight left from Finian.

The two of them thus gained the anteroom before panic broke out. There, unfortunately, things did not go so smoothly.

This was entirely due to a pale youth in spectacles who had been left on the door and whose nerves were obviously stretched to breaking point in anticipation of violence. When he saw Kevin striding towards him he lost control completely, picked up a chair and threw it. In the slight pause thus engineered, the thugs leapt to action. The result was chaos.

If there had been any doubt that Kevin was the object of the attack it was swiftly dispelled; they all made for him as one man. At the same moment a shillelagh appeared in Finian's hand, whirling like a catherine wheel.

Kevin saw the shillelagh crack down on the head of the leading tough, saw the second one leap past, saw the wicked glint of a razor blade and Finian's face contorted in a shout of warning. Then someone switched out the light.

Kevin ducked, dived for the refreshment table, missed it and landed against the tea urn, which was extremely hot.

The lights went on again. He caught a brief glimpse of Finian laying about him—regardless, Kevin feared, of friend or foe. He also saw that the bearlike young member of the United Freedom Movement was strangling somebody in the corner. One of the thugs was wielding a chair like a medieval mace; he saw Kevin by the refreshment table and made for him. Kevin picked up a huge pot of scalding hot coffee and flung it. The lights went out for the second time.

Now somebody was blowing a whistle. The refreshment table went over with an avalanche of broken crockery. A young woman's voice was screaming really shocking vernacular. A hurtling body struck Kevin on the shoulders, knocking him over, and at the same moment somebody

217

else reached the switch. Again the carnage was lit. Now, however, the room seemed to be full of police. Kevin saw that one of them was sitting on the floor holding his head; he caught a gleam of satisfaction in Finian's eye.

In the midst of all this, never for an instant losing the look of a mild dominie, stood Farquarson. He waved casually to Kevin and pointed towards the door.

One of the guard was remonstrating with the bearlike advocate of freedom. The latter still held in a great hand the limp but struggling thug whom Kevin and Finian had struck at on their way out. All in all this man seemed to have got the worst end of the entire fracas. The bear seemed unwilling to release him.

It was as Kevin moved to obey Farquarson's indication of the door that a sudden skirmish broke out once more in his corner. The whole thing happened quickly. He caught a glimpse of the old vulture with someone trying to re-strain him. The vulture was shouting, "Nonpolitical, d'you understand? We brook no violence." And he then, much to that young man's surprise, struck Kevin very hard indeed on top of the head with an empty whisky bottle. Kevin passed out at once.

It was an inglorious end to an otherwise successful battle, but in an oblique way it solved the whole problem. For in the fantastic dream world of his coma, or in the semicon-sciousness which followed it, or in some waking thought re-leased by the blow, Kevin remembered exactly what it was he knew about the orange board on which was written in bold black letters, *Tara Lounge*.

## IV

FIRST OF ALL he saw Celia's face; it came swimming out of a spiral of darkness, and about it there flickered an aurora borealis of blinding light. Presently the darkness and the aurora sorted themselves out into recognizable shapes—into the comfortable reality of Uncle Edward Dillon's library and into shadowy figures standing about it. He was conscious again, and Celia was stroking his forehead with cool fingers; she also smelled most delectable.

After this, although his head was aching unbearably, he became aware of the world about him. He saw, beyond her cool young face, the figures of Farquarson, Finian, and old Edward Dillon. They were all watching him with varying expressions of concern. There was a stranger present, also; a doctor, it seemed. He took Kevin's pulse, felt his forehead, examined his eyes, and said, "The sooner he's in bed the better. The sedative will begin to work soon, and you can give him two more when he's tucked up. I'll call again in the morning." Then he wavered away into the shadows, and at once—so powerful is suggestion—Kevin

219

could feel the sedative claiming him. He had not much wish to stay awake in any case; it was pleasanter to lie there dozing, with Celia stroking his forehead. The aurora borealis was beginning again.

Perhaps he slept. Certainly, when he next opened his eyes, he saw Inspector O'Connor looking at him. He heard the crisp voice say, "In any case I thought you'd want to know straight away; the two you managed to get hold of are pretty well known to us. Of course they won't talk. One of them nearly had the life shaken out of him anyway and the other got a severe sort of a crack over the head . . ."

Kevin sat up suddenly, his brain splitting. Finian and Uncle Edward were no longer present. Farquarson and O'Connor looked at him in astonishment; Celia was trying to make him stay still.

"I—" he began. And knew that he had no idea of what he'd been going to say. He stared blankly; the two policemen stared back.

"Come on," said Celia. "Lie down. The bed's being made up for you; it won't be long now."

Obediently Kevin lay down and closed his eyes.

Farquarson's voice said, "We could, I suppose, get a list of all the people in Dublin who hold a license for short-wave transmitters."

"Certainly," replied O'Connor. "But ten to one the fellows you're after wouldn't be on it, for one reason or another."

Farquarson swore gently.

"Mind you," the Irishman went on, "I'd take a bet you're

on the wrong track in any case . . ." His voice faded away.

Kevin knew that he had something important to say, but he could not think what it was. Snatches of their conversation came to him.

O'Connor: ". . . nothing to be gained by exhumation, even if we could get the permit . . . Unrecognizable to all intents and purposes . . . No doubt in my mind that Lawlor's dead—no doubt at all. . . ."

And Farquarson: ". . . but, my dear laddie, by that time it'll be too late. The Foreign Office takes . . . And by tomorrow evening at the latest . . ."

O'Connor: ". . . mind you, I'd like to help, but what chance is there of . . ."

Farquarson: "Well, we got a couple of them for you."

"Mercenaries. Hired roughs. Anything for a bit of cash. Certainly not Communists, anyway. Timmy Duggan's a Catholic, and a staunch one; he'd murder, but he'd never deny the Church. You're on the wrong track. . . ."

Presently the voices faded away down the long spiral of darkness until they were no more than whispers in another room.

Later, there were arms round him; he was lifted. He was walking upstairs supported on both sides. Out of darkness Celia bent over to give him two pink capsules with a glass of warm water. She kissed his forehead—soft touch like petals of a flower—and then backed away into the darkness.

Kevin sighed and let himself float out onto a great, calm sea of sleep. All the weariness of the past days and nights fell away into the dark water, and he lay staring up at a sky of eternal stars. . . .

Presently he was not even aware of dreams and fantasies. He was in a deep, drugged, exhausted slumber.

He had known when he stepped off the plane a devastating sense of nightmare repetition. When he awoke suddenly to find Celia sitting in an armchair watching him, he knew that the repetition had really *been* a nightmare: he was back in the Queens Hotel in Birmingham. In a moment she would tell him that she must go to Liverpool, and in Liverpool there would be a terrific fire . . .

For a moment, caught in the no man's land between sleeping and waking, he was really frightened of this glimpse of eternity. Then, abruptly, it was swept away in a thunderous wave of realization. He knew what it was he had wanted to tell Farquarson.

Celia, seeing him suddenly spring bolt-upright into a sitting position, thought that his brain might have been touched by the blow. There was little sanity in his eyes, and he kept saying, "Got it. Got it. Oh, my sainted Aunt Fanny." She ran to him, trying to press him down onto the pillows again. But he, eyes wild with excitement, shouted, "Where's Farquarson? What's the time?"

"It's four o'clock," said Celia. "The doctor came but you were asleep. The sedative must have been pretty strong. He said you were to stay in bed until he'd seen you. He said you were on no account . . ."

But Kevin was in the middle of the room looking for his shirt.

"Four o'clock!" he was shouting. "You let me sleep till

four—today of all days. It wasn't a sedative; it was an anaesthetic."

She ran to him then and held him by the arms. "Oh, what does the *day* matter? You're ill. You may harm yourself."

He was arrested, staring at her.

"Consolidate C," he quoted.

"Damn 'Consolidate C,'" said Celia fiercely. "Go back to bed; you may have concussion. I told Dr. Brien you'd be like this."

Kevin—though quite aware of the possibility of concussion, for his head was hurting abominably—had no intention of going back to bed. He found time, however, to be pleased at her very evident concern for his welfare.

"Farquarson," he said. "I've got to see Farquarson."

"But you *can't*," Celia insisted. "He's gone to some headquarters or other; he's trying to arrange for a direction-finding unit. He told me to see that you didn't go out alone."

"Oh, did he?" replied Kevin, struggling into his shirt. "Well, turn your back. I'm taking off my trousers."

"Leave it to him," said Celia, staring at the wall. "It's his job, not yours."

Kevin snorted. "First of all you try and stop me because you don't want Stephen Lawlor hurt. Now you try and stop me because you don't want *me* hurt."

With every movement he made, he was becoming increasingly aware that Celia and the doctor were right: he felt ghastly. But he must, he *must* go and see if this revelation of what he had seen in his drunken stupor were true. Concussion or no concussion, he must go and see.

223

"Listen," he said, "I'm going to a pub called the Tara Lounge; it's down the quay—on the south side—you can't miss it. You've got to get hold of Farquarson somehow, as soon as possible. Tell him where I am; tell him to meet me there; tell him I think I've got a clue—the one we've been waiting for."

"But how . . ." Celia began.

Kevin, buttoning his jacket, laughed a trifle wildly. "I knew all the time," he said. "It's crazy, but I did." He made for the door. "I was drunk," he added—an, to her, unintelligible parting shot.

Before she could reach the top of the stairs the front door had slammed behind him.

There will be a door, Kevin told himself as he hurried along the busy streets in an ecstasy of excitement. It is about two yards to the left of the door leading into the Tara Lounge, and the wall in which it stands is set back from the wall of the pub about three feet. Over the door is a fanlight, and on the left of it a row of dirty brass plates with individual bells. If the door is open, I shall see an inner porch with another door, and this one has glass panels. The inner porch is painted a dull kind of Venetian red. Since the entrance to the Tara Lounge is placed on a corner of the building, it is at an angle of forty-five degrees to the door of the next building—the building which looks like a down-at-heel block of offices. . . .

It was all clear to him, as clear in detail as a contact print from a precisely exposed negative. As he turned off O'Connell Bridge down the quay, his excitement almost blinded him; he could disregard completely the fierce pain in his

224

head and the weakness of his legs. He knew, he *knew* that he was right; everything could be explained at last.

He could see, far away down the quay, the orange and black sign of the public house. Away to the left of it, masts and yards and superstructures made an intricate, exciting pattern against a pearly, Canaletto-like sky. He quickened pace, aware of something like antagonism in his legs, which were slow to obey him. His head hurt abominably. But only one thing mattered. It seemed, suddenly, that the faster he moved, the farther away the orange board became. He felt like Alice in the garden, sprinting in order to stay where she was.

And now, at last, he was drawing level with the Tara Lounge. In two seconds—in five more paces . . .

He stopped and stared, his breath coming in gasps, for he had been practically running all the way.

Yes, it was just as he had known it would be. The entrance to the bar at an angle and the wall of the next house set back a few feet. And there, in that wall, the door with the fanlight and the brass plates; the hallway painted dull red; the inner door with glass panels. Here—in that humiliating semicoma induced by raw, rasping alcohol, which he had thought to be whisky—here, lolling helplessly on Mr. Shaun O'Farrell's arm while the world spun round him, he had seen Stephen Lawlor, he had looked across at the red doorway, and had caught—by some wicked quirk of chance—a brief glimpse of Stephen Lawlor: so brief a glimpse that it had barely impressed itself on his reeling brain. But that was what had happened, all right: he had seen Lawlor alive *after* Lawlor had been killed. And it was this chance

225

which had started the whole unwieldy juggernaut on its catastrophic downhill run.

Doubtless Lawlor had realized that he, Kevin, was drunk; but could he be sure that he had not been recognized? For if he had been recognized, his whole plan was in danger. How he must have struggled with this terrible problem, seeing all too clearly its dangerous possibilities. How he must have lain awake that night, sweating, wondering whether he could leave it to chance that Kevin had been too drunk to know what he had seen. And sometime in the cold dawn he must have realized that he could never rest until this threat had been removed—just as the threat of Percy Williamson had been removed.

Only when he had failed, twice, to kill Kevin did he turn to that last, doomed resort. He had shown himself to the man whose word or whose silence could ruin or save him; he had invented that fairy tale to explain why he was still alive. But already, because Kevin had not believed him, he was facing failure; that meeting of eyes in the doorway of a public house had doomed him to failure.

Yes, Kevin understood it plainly now. He understood how it all hung on this last link—the thing in his brain which he had known and not known. A paradox. The last link, holding the whole weight of what had happened afterwards.

Carried forward on the elation and excitement of discovery, Kevin did not for a moment doubt that somewhere in the house confronting him he would find a wireless transmitter, and possibly Stephen Lawlor as well. Perhaps he was still suffering from that blow on the head; perhaps he *was* concussed. Certainly he felt no sense of fear as he crossed the pavement, mounted the stone steps under the fanlight, and entered the red hallway. The second door was not locked. He pushed it open and went in.

## V

THE HOUSE had once been an office building. It gave the impression of having been condemned, of awaiting demolition. Possibly one or two of the offices were still used occasionally for the transacting of dockside business. There was a smell of decay; a dead silence.

He went straight upstairs, ignoring the first, second and third floors. At the back of his mind was a certainty that what he looked for would be at the top of the house.

When he had climbed the last flight he found, instead of the expected attic landing, a long corridor stretching away into darkness. A dirty window showed him back yards and roofs and tottering chimneys. Another, halfway along the corridor, looked out onto the quay and the river. He noticed that this was the last of the big houses; it had doubtless been built by some eighteenth century merchant. Beyond it were the crouching hovels of Victorian slumdom, timber and coal depots, an occasional warehouse. He noticed also that on the jetty below dockers were going home from work.

The silence of the place was oppressive. He was suddenly very much aware of the pounding of his own heart. He went quickly down the corridor. At the end of it was a sharp right turn. He paused at the corner listening, felt for his revolver and released the safety catch. The ache in his head had lifted now; he felt only unreal, as if walking in a dream. It was a sensation he had grown to associate with Dublin; he was used to it.

No sound reached him. He did not like the corner at all, but it had to be rounded sometime. He took his courage in both hands, moved swiftly—and nearly fell down a flight of stairs. He paused again, listening. . . . Could he, or could he not hear voices? The gradual rise and fall of men's voices speaking confidentially? He went down the stairs with extreme caution. At the bottom were two doors, one ajar, giving onto blackness, the other closed. On the closed door was a notice. It read, *Dublin Wireless Friendship Society*. A club crest, using the initials *D.W.F.S.*, was fixed over it, and in a frame, hung to the left of it, was the official post office permit licensing the Dublin Wireless Friendship Society to use a transmitter on the premises.

By now Kevin's heart was threatening to leap out of his mouth, but his brain was quite clear and controlled. He only regretted having no torch.

As far as he could see the open door led to an empty room, used perhaps for stores. There was an electric light switch, but no bulb. He stood half in the doorway listening.

Unless someone on the premises of the D.W.F.S. was either asleep or completely dumb there were only two men in there. One had a high, slightly nasal tone and spoke with an Irish accent; the other, deeper voice belonged to an

229

Englishman. Kevin waited, listening, but he could hear no word of what they said. Occasionally their conversation was interrupted by the twittering sound of Morse, and once the higher of the two voices was raised in clear, radio phraseology. It said, "This is Victor, this is Victor. I hear you strength five. Strength five. Over."

Kevin began to grow impatient. He wondered where the hell Farquarson had got to. Two of them could by now have taken over the set, he was sure of that. Alone, it was too risky.

However, after he had waited for twenty minutes, impatience began to get the better of him; and his particular brand of impatience was not always the best guide, even if it had shown him the right course at the United Freedom meeting. But, as he was reaching out for the door handle, he heard the deeper voice speak almost in his ear; its owner had moved to the door. "No fear," it said. "It's my night on tomorrow, and I'm keeping out of the way till then. So long." And Kevin only just had time to beat a hasty retreat into the darkness before the door opened and a dark-haired, stocky man came out onto the landing.

The high voice said, "Well, see if you can find Bert. I've been tied to this bloody thing since midday; it's time he had a go."

The other grunted, closed the door and clattered upstairs and along the corridor.

When the sound of his departure had dwindled away, Kevin took a firm grip on his revolver and tried the door again. He was relieved to find that it was not locked, as doubtless it should have been, but he waited a moment before entering. Presently he heard the welcome stutter of

Morse, which would mean, presumably, that the operator would be busily engaged reading it. Then he opened the door swiftly but silently and went in.

The man must have seen movement out of the corner of his eye, for he swung round, pencil poised; the headphones slipped off his ears. It was, Kevin was pleased to see, the rat-faced individual who had waited for him in the foyer of the Melbourne. Unfortunately for him the cord of the headphones had wound itself round his neck so that when he leapt convulsively to avoid Kevin's assault he nearly succeeded in hanging himself. In any case it was a brief scuffle, and he went down tidily after the first blow from the revolver butt. Kevin, unused to such swashbuckling, hoped that he had not struck too hard. He wasted no time, however. There was a good deal of spare cord lying about and it lent itself admirably to strong, tight knots. In a few minutes Ratface was trussed up and gagged with his own black insulating tape. He was, Kevin discovered, somewhat to his surprise, still breathing.

The stocky man had sounded as though he would not be returning that day. The danger, of course, was that he might indeed find the man called Bert and send him to take over from Ratface. The important thing therefore was speed.

Kevin had learnt Morse in the Navy, and once learnt it is not easily forgotten. Reading, he remembered, needed constant practice, but sending was another matter; and in this case he only needed to send.

Presumably the Dublin Wireless Friendship Society, hidden away in its disused building, had been left alone by both police and post office. Great pains must have been

231

taken to establish it as a bona-fide radio club long before it was used for its real purpose. And in any case, as Kevin knew all too well, the signals which it originated, though in code, were the most harmless-sounding missives imaginable. Doubtless there was a set of neat explanations to be given in case of enquiry. Besides which it did not require more than a glance round the room to realize that the whole place could be abandoned at a moment's notice.

Kevin got down to work quickly. Now, because he knew what he was looking for, it did not take him long to find the current code and to check it, for certainty, with the most recent message lying on the table. He then locked the door and settled down to his job.

First he wrote out the message in plain language. "To all stations," it read. "From Victor. DJ121. Police active. Abandon ABC. Scatter. Am closing down finally."

It was possibly not what Vera, Olga, and the rest of them would expect; in fact there would almost certainly be a special code word to cover the situation. On the other hand, people often forget procedure in a grave emergency, and the message he had invented would spread panic if nothing else—that and the silence which was to follow it.

He had now wasted ten minutes of valuable time. Moreover he was beginning to realize the really startling danger of his position, which, in the excitement of discovery, he had conveniently ignored. By the time he was halfway through the coding of the message, sweat was running down his back. He knew that in emergency plain language was always used, but he knew that in this case the code would add just that touch of conviction which might make all the difference between success and failure. He bent

232

every nerve in his body to combat increasing panic; if he lost his head and made a mistake it would spoil the whole manoeuvre. And so he sat there, hands clammy, shirt clinging to his back, concentrating furiously on the maze of elusive figures, while the headphones went on with their stuttering and the clock ticked by agonizing minutes.

Finally, when it was done, he had to wait in a fury of impatience until the air was clear. He knew enough of wireless to recognize that this was essential.

At last, at long last, there was a moment's silence, and he dived into it with the first group of his message. And, oh, how heavy, ham-fisted, unbiddable were his fingers after long disuse. He knew that he must not hurry at all costs or his Morse would go to pieces. And so he tapped carefully away at it, making each letter as clear as he could, each group concise. When he had finished, he did not wait for acknowledgements, but started straight away to repeat his message.

He was three groups from the end when he heard footsteps approaching along the corridor. Even then, fixed in concentration, he did not give way to fear. His heart thundered and his hand shook, but he kept going, evenly and steadily, revolver clasped in his left hand, eyes moving swiftly from the pad to the door and back again.

The handle turned now and whoever it was leaned against the thin panelling. The door shuddered, but stood firm.

Kevin tapped out the last letter of the last group, and at the same moment heard the chink of keys on a ring. A key was inserted in the latch, the latch grated; but, of

233

course, Kevin had slid the bolt. Again weight was thrown against the door and something splintered.

Kevin, glancing wildly round, saw a heavy wooden beam in the corner; it had broken off the contraption that opened the skylight. He seized it, raised it above his head and brought it smacking down into the entrails of the transmitter. There was a blue flash, a puff of smoke, an unholy smashing of glass and buckling of metal. He laid about him then, demolishing everything in sight. At the same time the door began to splinter. Whoever was battering at it swore explosively and redoubled his efforts. Kevin dropped the baulk of timber and turned to face the onslaught, gun in hand. As he did so—and only a fraction of a second before the thin panels gave way—he recognized the voice. Then the door reeled back and he stood face to face with Stephen Lawlor.

For a long, long time they confronted each other in silence. Lawlor's eyes took in the shattered room: the tangle of wires which had once been a wireless transmitter; the wrecked receiver on its side amid a flurry of paper; the bound and gagged figure lying on the floor. A faint blue haze of smoke hung in the still air, and there was a smell of burnt rubber. Kevin never took his eyes off the pale, handsome face, watching each detail of demolition register there. He was surprised to find that he still held, clenched in his hand, the message he had just sent. He held out the two crumpled sheets of paper—the plain-language and the coded version. Lawlor took them in silence. Although he appeared to be unarmed, Kevin kept him covered; he was taking no more chances.

234

Lawlor read the message quickly, glanced up, eyes very bright, and then read it again. This time he stared hard at the paper for a long time. When he finally raised his face there was an odd expression on it which Kevin could not, as yet, understand.

And still they did not speak. That seemingly endless silence went on, and on, and on. For the first time since he had entered the house Kevin became aware of outside noises. A tug pooped on the river and a deep siren answered. There was a rattle of heavy cable.

At last a shadow of the old Lawlor smile flitted over the taut features, and he spoke.

"I'm going to put my hand in my pocket," he said, flickering his fingers. "Don't shoot me."

"I shall shoot you instantly," replied Kevin, "if you make any move of any sort."

Lawlor shrugged. "Then you can put your hand in my pocket for me. You'll find a gun there. This side. My jacket. It's no use to me."

Kevin was astounded, but managed to say evenly, "All right. Turn your back and I'll take it. But I warn you— one move, and I'll kill you."

Lawlor turned and Kevin advanced warily. He was surprised to find that the gun really did exist. He transferred it to his own pocket.

"Now," Lawlor said, "I'd like a cigarette."

"Go ahead. No tricks."

Again the faint smile. "A born romantic," he said. "May I go to the window? It's stuffy in here."

"To signal for help?"

"No. To look out."

"Yes. If you keep your hands at your sides."

"I'll do that." He went to the long window which ran across one wall of the room, perched himself on the sill and glanced down at the quay. Kevin did not move from his position covering the door. He was at a loss, unsure of himself—unsure of this man's odd mood and of his long silence. He could not stifle an ugly feeling that he was trapped. And, as the minutes wore on and nothing happened, this feeling increased until his nerves were all on edge, strident with fear of the unknown.

Lawlor stared out of the window. He seemed to have sunk into a quite inexplicable repose, but his face was still taut and unutterably weary.

Finally, Kevin could no longer bear the silence. He said, "You don't seem particularly eager to get away. Do you realize the game's up? You're trapped."

The other turned his head slowly, as if roused from sleep. His voice was quite controlled and casual, which only served to accentuate Kevin's disquiet. "I suppose I am trapped," he said. And, after another long pause, he added, "A lot depends on who the next person is to appear at the bottom of those stairs. *Everything* might be said to depend on it."

"Meaning?"

"Meaning," said Lawlor slowly, "whether the third party is—is yours or mine."

Instinctively Kevin's hand touched his pocket where the gun lay.

"That," Lawlor added, "is of no use to me either way." He was silent again. Time seemed to stand stock-still, and yet Kevin, glancing nervously at the clock, saw that he

236

had already been in this room for an hour and ten minutes. Outside the window a change had already come over the sky. Afternoon was merging gently into evening. And nothing happened.

Another ten minutes—ten minutes like eternity—went by. At the end of it Kevin said, "I'm getting you out of here. Come on."

Lawlor glanced at him sideways. "I may be wrong," he said, "but I've an idea that if either of us puts a foot outside the door of this house we stand a good chance of being shot. I don't think I'd risk it, if I were—" He broke off abruptly, eyes wide. Kevin had heard it, too: the unmistakable sound of a board creaking somewhere down that long corridor. A flicker of fear ran up his spine and caressed the back of his neck. Lawlor stood up, listening. Their eyes met.

Now, carefully, someone was coming down the last flight of stairs. Kevin raised his gun, tensed himself, eyes flickering from Lawlor to the door and back again. If this was the stocky man with the deep voice returning, he knew that his time was up. His mouth, he noticed, had gone quite dry.

The bottom stair creaked and Celia stood confronting him.

"For heaven's sake," snapped Kevin, nerves jangling, "get out of here."

She shook her head. "No. I— Farquarson sent me. He sent me to tell you to stay here till he comes."

At the sound of her voice Stephen Lawlor sank back once more onto the window ledge.

Kevin said, "Farquarson! He must be mad. Where is he?"

"Outside at the moment." She came slowly into the room, her dark eyes fixed on him. "Are you all right?"

"Yes."

Only then did she turn her head—slowly, as if forcing it round against its will—to look at Stephen Lawlor. For a time they stared at each other.

The dead unreality of a dream had returned, and Kevin found himself caught in it. Neither Celia nor Lawlor said anything, but he sensed that in their stare they were reliving a whole lifetime of intimate moments. The thought racked him, but he knew that he must not break their silence. He knew that in this moment something was surely dying inside her—dying a cruel death. Her face was very pale, and she could not hide the anguish she was feeling.

Lawlor saw this, too. Warmth suddenly crept into his eyes; he leaned forward and began to speak quietly, urgently. "Celia," he said. "Celia, you could help me. You're the only person who could do it; he wouldn't shoot you. Come here."

Kevin swore out loud and took a pace forward. Only one pace. He was arrested by something strange and terrible: the girl was trembling, and there were tears in her eyes. "Oh, Steve," she said. "Oh, Steve."

"Only you," Lawlor went on. "He wouldn't shoot you. Come here, Celia. Do this last thing for me. Celia—" His voice was warm, intimate, charged with an overpowering, desperate sincerity. He was using every ounce of his incredible charm, the whole weight of his sexual magnetism. It was a frightening, a revolting performance. And the true

238

horror of it lay in the fact that Celia, knowing all she knew, trembled and went pale before the assault. For one hideous moment Kevin thought that all which was most inexplicable in woman would capitulate.

But he underestimated her. She controlled herself by a visible, violent effort. Gradually that trembling ceased; her face hardened, became ugly as Kevin would never have believed it could be ugly. In a dead husk of her real voice she said, "Oh, shoot him, John. He's mad."

To Lawlor her tone was clearly a slap in the face; he looked almost absurdly surprised, and it struck Kevin that this was possibly the first time the charm had ever failed him with a woman.

At that moment footsteps rang confidently in the corridor. Farquarson's voice called out, "It's all right, it's only me. Don't fash yourselves."

He appeared, homely and quite unimpressive, in the doorway, bland face blank, hat pushed back on his head. He glanced round the chaos of the room with a small, dry smile. "Good laddie," he said. "Good laddie. Who's this?" He rolled the bound man over with his foot. Kevin noticed that the small eyes were now wide open; it still surprised him that his victim was not dead.

"Hm," said Farquarson, and he looked at Stephen Lawlor. Then he said, "Hm," again. And added, "Well, Mr. Kevin, let's untie our skinny friend here."

"Untie him!"

"That's what I said, laddie."

Kevin, after a moment's puzzled hesitation, knelt down and set to work on the cord. Soon Ratface was sitting up, rubbing his wrists and ankles. As soon as the black tape fell away from his mouth words came tumbling out in a torrent.

"It wasn't me," he said. "I didn't do it. The chap turned up here and started blathering about how he'd picked up the messages in England. I didn't do it. I just sent for Mr. Lawlor. They went off together. I didn't do it . . ."

"All right, all right. I believe you." Farquarson dammed the flow. "Now stand up."

The man struggled shakily to his feet, supporting himself on the table.

"You can go," said Farquarson, "when your legs'll carry you."

"Go!" burst out Kevin. He was silenced by a glare from the policeman's generally mild eyes.

"Mr. Lawlor here will give you permission, I've no doubt."

But Lawlor was staring intently out of the window. Something below on the quay had gripped his attention. After a moment he turned and looked at Farquarson—a long look as if some sort of secret bound them together.

Farquarson nodded. "You like the view?"

"It's— It's the one I expected to see."

"Would you like this man to go?"

"Yes. Why not? It won't make any difference now."

Ratface hesitated. "What— What shall I say?"

Lawlor turned away. "You know what you'll say. You've got eyes in your head. You've got a brain."

Ratface sidled towards the door, then turned and ran for it. The sound of his scampering feet, sounding very like the rodent he so closely resembled, died away in the quiet house.

It was Kevin who broke the silence. "What *is* all this? Will someone enlighten me?"

Lawlor give him a pitying look and shrugged. "Luck was on your side," he commented. "You couldn't possibly have got me otherwise."

Farquarson answered the question less obliquely. He gestured towards the window, and Kevin, who had for so long been rooted to one part of the floor that he had almost forgotten how to leave it, went over and looked out.

The first blue mist of twilight lay over the quayside and the river. It softened the shadows thrown by the day's last sunlight—a thick golden light catching the spars of the ships and turning the domed Customs House across the river into a fabled palace. He couldn't remember ever having seen the river look so serene and beautiful, and it was the more beautiful in that the sunlight was fleeting; the city was cupped in darkness, for it was an overcast evening. He saw nothing else, but stood there caught in some kind of reaction to his moment of violence. He could almost have cried because it was so beautiful after the ugliness which had happened.

"Well?" said Farquarson.

"It's a lovely evening."

At this Stephen Lawlor laughed; he raised his head and laughed loudly and frighteningly. For him, as Kevin realized later, it was a monstrously good joke. A monstrous joke, anyway.

The laughter died suddenly into a waiting silence.

Lawlor said, "Who'd have known romantics were so dangerous?" He stood up and looked at Farquarson. "I suppose you want *me* to go now, don't you?"

The policeman nodded, eyes very bright. "In your own time, laddie," he said.

"But . . ." Kevin began.

"It'll be all the same," Lawlor interrupted, "whether I go now or later."

Kevin was quiet suddenly. He did not understand yet, but he sensed that this was something between the other two men.

"I'd like to hold you," Farquarson said. "Another couple of days and we'd have had official co-operation from the guard. As it is—"

Lawlor almost smiled. "You wouldn't have got me to talk. I'm no traitor."

"Traitor!" echoed the policeman wonderingly.

Lawlor straightened himself with an effort, so weary now that it was painful for Kevin to look at him. Celia was not even trying to look at him.

"Yes, traitor. When you've spent a lifetime believing in nothing, it's—it's a revelation to find a belief. It's a release. A—" He raised his arms and let them drop to his sides again. "A miracle."

"And you still believe in it?" That wondering tone had not left Farquarson's voice.

"Of course. What difference does my future make? Thousands have failed, but it still goes on. Millions will die for it. I'm only one of them." He looked proud suddenly —and, strangely, he no longer seemed weary.

"Ha!" snapped Farquarson, his voice sharp once more. "A day will dawn, eh?"

"Yes. A day will dawn. Laugh if you like. It isn't funny."

"Certainly not for you."

Lawlor gave a faint shudder.

Kevin, looking out of the window, saw something which made his breath catch in his throat. He saw a man standing in the shadow of a pile of crates on the jetty—and another leaning against a railway wagon—a third, showing only his head and shoulders above a huge coil of hawser. Suddenly it seemed that the shadows were alive. He said, "This house is being watched. We're in a trap."

Lawlor sighed.

"*We* aren't," said Farquarson. "They aren't interested in us any more."

"You mean—"

The policeman, with something like compassion in his eyes, was watching Stephen Lawlor. Twilight had seeped into the wrecked room; all their faces were cold and mask-like. The sun had gone.

Farquarson said, "They're waiting for Mr. Lawlor here. News travels fast in the world he inhabits, particularly news of failure."

Celia gave a little moan and turned away from them.

"But," said Kevin, comprehension dawning, "we can't let them *kill* him."

Farquarson made a small gesture of hopelessness. "We can't stop them."

"But the police . . ."

"The guard," replied Farquarson, "are not in on this. I knew the Foreign Office would be too slow."

"Isn't there a back way out?"

"There is. That's being watched, too."

"But surely . . ."

243

"Why," said Stephen Lawlor wearily, "all this sudden regard for my safety? I'm perfectly ready to go out to them. It's true: I've failed. Failure is only regarded as a virtue by the English. We—" He hesitated. "We are not English."

They were all silent, appalled by his calm acceptance. The twilight, coming in with heavy cloud, had thickened perceptibly; it was almost dark.

"You don't understand," Lawlor said. "You'll go on not understanding until it's too late. I believe in this thing; I'm perfectly willing to die for it. Thousands of men and women have died for it in the past; thousands more are going to die for it in the future."

"I think," said Farquarson gently, "that we won't have any propaganda, Mr. Lawlor."

Outside the window twilight looked very cold suddenly. Stephen Lawlor turned and walked out of the room. They heard his footsteps go slowly up the stairs and along the corridor. Once he paused. Perhaps he was listening, or perhaps his nerve failed him for a moment.

Farquarson, almost apologetically, said, "We couldn't have held him anyway—not in a foreign country with no direct evidence."

"I—don't understand," said Kevin. "How did they—" he nodded down at the waiting shadows on the quay— "know so quickly."

"I saw to it." The policeman's voice was grim. "One of the men we picked up in the fight last night was the type who'll do anything for money. In this case he passed on some information for us."

"About Lawlor?"

"About his—mistakes, yes. It's not difficult to set these people at each other's throats. It's what you might call poetic justice, isn't it? After all, that's how they go to work—setting people at each other's throats." He sounded weary. Disgusted. "That little rat of a wireless operator didn't waste time, either. They don't trust each other, you see. They're all spies, all afraid. That's why the whole thing will fail in the end. You can't build empires on mistrust."

The shadows on the quay seemed to tremble suddenly. Kevin caught his breath, and Celia turned to him convulsively, burying her face in his coat. He put his two arms round her, held her tight as if protecting her from all the violence and evil in the world.

The foreshortened figure of Stephen Lawlor came into view, walking slowly, head up. Kevin saw him as the enigma he had always known him to be—a murderer; generous to children whom he loved quite selflessly; a man capable of organizing death for hundreds, penury for thousands; capable of risking his life to save an unknown sailor.

Unpredictable.

He walked out onto the quay, not hurrying, not even afraid—or so it seemed. Then there was a sudden flurry of movement—a swift converging of shadows. The blade of a knife glinted. A shoe scraped on cobblestones. For a moment the dark figures swayed together in an ugly cluster. Then they fell apart, drew back, returned to the darkness which had spewed them up.

The body of Stephen Lawlor lay alone on the deserted quay.

245

Then, miraculously—in that moment before the shouting voices, the running footsteps, the shrilling police whistles—all the street lamps bloomed into light up and down the Liffey, glittering in the water, winking through the trees on the far bank. A sudden token of warmth in a cold world—a token of hope in a cold world.

"*John Kevin's Dublin*," wrote one of the critics, "is without doubt the least successful and the least popular of his remarkable series. Many of his admirers were dumbfounded to discover that for this artist in photography the 'fair city' of the ballad was a haunted place of strange shadows and grotesque images. Bizarre. Often downright sinister. Exactly why it appeared to him in this light must remain a mystery, since he refuses to explain himself.

"His new book on Venice is another matter altogether, and it is by far the best he has done. Here are gaiety, elegance and beauty captured unerringly and breath-takingly. Here, too, are depth and perception, instead of the mere cleverness which we had come to expect. Mr. Kevin has grown up.

"There has, I understand, been some conjecture regarding the identity of the enchanting young lady with the fair hair who appears in certain of the Venetian pictures. The curious, one would have thought, need not look far for a clue—a clue also, I fancy, to Mr. Kevin's new depth of feeling. The book is dedicated 'To My Wife.'"